A Soldier Erect

A Soldier Erect

BRIAN W. ALDISS

COWARD, McCANN & GEOGHEGAN, INC.

NEW YORK

Contents

For my friends in Japan and India —
made since these ancient embarrassments

As she turned around, I saw part of her backside, leaned over and laid my face on it, crying about my broken drum; the evening sunshine made it all bright – how strange I should recollect that so clearly, but I have always recollected sunshine.

My Secret Life, by 'Walter'

'Cavaliers, and strong men, this cavalier is the friend of a friend of mine. *Es mucho hombre*. There is none like him in Spain. He speaks the crabbed Gitano though he is an Inglesite.

'We do not believe it,' replied several grave voices. 'It is not possible.'

The Bible in Spain, by George Borrow

book 1
The Lair of the Monkey God

AS THE LAST PARTY-GUESTS WERE GROPING their way into the blackout, I belted upstairs and shut myself in my bedroom. My dressing-gown fell off its hook as the door slammed, dropping like a dying man, one arm melodramatically over the bed. I dragged my sports-jacket off my shoulders, rolled it into a bundle, and flung it into the far corner of the room, all of ten feet away.

On the top of the chest-of-drawers stood a carved bear, given to me on my tenth birthday by an uncle lately back from Switzerland, a bag of green apples, a framed photograph of Ida Lupino, my uniform dress cap, and three woollen vests. I swept them all off and climbed on to the chest-of-drawers, where I squatted, groaning and rolling my head from side to side.

God, what sodding, shagging, scab-devouring misery it all was! The humiliation – the *ignobility* – of the whole shitting shower! The creepy, crappy narrowness of my parents' life! And that was supposed to be my embarkation leave party before I went abroad to serve my king and cunting country! If that was embarkation leave, roll on bloody germ warfare!

By kneeling up a little on the chest-of-drawers, I could press my head and shoulders against the ceiling and so re-semble a deformed caryatid. Thinking vicious army thoughts,

I pushed one side of my face against the flaking ceiling. My jaw slumped down, my tongue dripped saliva, my eyelids flickered like an ancient horror film, revealing acres of white-of-eye. At the same time, I managed to tremble and twitch in every muscle. Jesus, what a wet dream of a party that was! Party? I asked aloud, in tones of incredulity. Paaarty? Paaaa-ha-ha-ha-rty? Paaaa-urrgh-harty?

And I thought of the other blokes in 'A' Company. Their genial and loutish faces drifted before my inner eye, their blunt noses and short haircuts almost welcoming . . . Wally, Enoch, Geordie, old Chalkie White, Carter the Farter, Chota Morris . . . Tonight, they'd all be getting hopelessly pissed or screwing girls – or so they would stoutly claim when we got back to barracks tomorrow. And I – I, sober and un-stuffed, would have to lie to save my face, to subscribe to the infantry myth that one spent one's whole leave yarking it up some willing bit of stuff in a pub yard. I cramped my shoulders harder against the ceiling, hoping that I might burst through the lath-and-plaster into the gales of the false roof and erupt against the lagged water-tank. You mean to say that was the best they could do in the way of a party? For me, for the conquering hero, for the pride of the sodding Mendips?

The whole idea had been a farce from the beginning. My father had never shown one flicker of enthusiasm. My brother Nelson had managed to wangle leave from Edin-burgh to see me – 'for the last time', as he expressed it – and the farewell party had been his idea. He had jockeyed the parents into it.

'It's not easy in wartime,' my father said, shaking his head. 'You youngsters don't understand. I'm on warden duty, too, this week.'

'Go on, Colonel Whale would let you have a bottle of whisky, since Horry's going overseas. It's a special occasion!'

'Whisky? I'm not having whisky! It'd spoil the party! You'd only get drunk!'

'That's what whisky is *for*, Daddy,' my sister Ann said, in her long-suffering voice. We'd become good at long-suffering voices, simply through imitation.

My mother quite liked the idea of a party if she could possibly scrounge the clothing coupons to buy a pretty dress. She felt so dowdy. That was one reason why she never wanted to see anyone these days. She looked unhappily round the sitting room which, despite many years of punishing Stubbsian teetotalism, still held a faint beery aroma, in memory of the days when the house had been an inn.

'It really needs a good spring-clean before anyone comes in here!' Mother said, looking willowy and wan, mutely asking always to be forgiven for some great unspoken fault. 'The windows look so awful with that sticky paper on them, and I just wish we could have some new curtains.'

Certainly the house did appear neglected, not only because of the war, but because my mother's nervous disease was gaining on her. Housework was beyond her, she claimed. She grew more willowy by the week, to our irritation.

Eventually, Nelson and Ann and I browbeat father into holding a cele-ha-ha-bration. Ann was sixteen; she burst into tears and said she would not let her brother go overseas unless he had a party first.

So who do you think turned up that evening, tramping dolefully up our steps and into the living room, to sit affrontedly about in their suits and complain of the tastelessness of sausages, the decline of moral standards, and the military failings of the Russians, the Australians, the Canadians, the Americans, and the French? Why, flakey-scalped little Mr Jeremy Church, father's head clerk from the bank, with his cream-puff-faced wife Irene, very free with her 'lakes' and 'dislakes'; and my grandma, getting on a bit now, but scoring a shrewd blow against the times in which we lived by revealing how sandbags were all filled with nothing but ordinary seaside sand; and the Moles from the grocery, prim but patriotic, bringing with them an old aunt of Mrs Mole's, who had been bombed out of her London flat and wasn't afraid to tell you about it; and mother's friend Mrs Lilly Crane, whose husband was in something-or-other, with her daughter Henrietta, sub-titled 'The Enigma' by Ann; and Nelson's current girl friend, Valerie, watching for Nelson's signal to scram as soon as convenient; and dear old Miss Lewis from next door who still went to church every Sunday, rain or shine, although she was pushing a hundred-and-something, or could it be two hundred-and-something?; and a sexy friend of Ann's, Sylvia Rudge. Sixteen of us all told, the only people left in the East Midlands that mortality and conscription had spared. A dead lively lot. Mother handed the dates round with her renowned Light Touch, smiling sadly in my direction as one and all offered their condolences that she was having her younger son snatched from her. More of a funeral than a celebration.

Average age of party – fifty? Ninety? Who cared? I crouched on my perch trying to work out when the visitors had last – if ever – had it in. It was hard to imagine that the females were penetrable or, if penetrable, that the males were capable of penetrating them. Did Mr Mole occasionally manage a subterranean passage up Mrs Mole, over a sack of demerara, under a flag-draped photo of Winnie with his two fingers in the air?

From my disadvantage point, I could watch my reflection in the mirror of the wardrobe, which stood near the door and opposite the chest-of-drawers. Now *there* was a born shagger, if ever I saw one, given the chance. I stuck my feet in the top (sock and handkerchief) drawer and spread my arms out along the ceiling. The sight reminded me of something. Pulling the hair down over my eyes, I pantomimed a corny crucifixion scene, with plenty of bleary and reproachful dekkos up at the plaster. 'My God, why hast thou forsaken me?' I looked more like Hitler throwing one of his fits than Christ in final aggs.

Why this obsession with Christ, for God's sake? Perhaps I'd *been* Christ in a previous existence – during my mid-teens, I had nursed a sneaking belief in the theory of re-incarnation. Oh Christ, don't let me have been Christ! I dropped the crucifixion act and made monkey faces at myself.

You could rule out all the women at the party straight away, except for Valerie, Henrietta Crane, and Sylvia. Valerie was Nelson's bit of crumpet, so that left Henrietta Crane and Sylvia. That'll show you how desperate I was, not to rule out Henrietta Crane straight away! The Enigma was in her mid-twenties – perhaps five years older than I. A heavily-powdered girl, or was it just that she had never been dusted?, who looked as if her clothes, flesh, eyes, hair, everything, were made out of a single ambiguous material – stale sponge cake, say. Even I, despite frequent practice shots, could not imagine her undressed, or even with her hair down. Did she ever run for a bus, or fart, or burst out laughing? Henrietta Crane was the sort of girl you didn't have to go near to know that her breath would smell of Kensitas cigarettes and Milk of Magnesia. You never find girls like that any more, thank God. They were all scrapped at the end of the war.

Which left our Syl. As the party warmed up – i.e., came to something approaching room-temperature – Ann was working our gramophone, then giving out with a Carroll Gibbons recording of *That Old Black Magic*, and Sylvia was standing beside her, jiffling to the tunes. It was a wind-up gramophone, brought out of the air-raid shelter now that we were not having air raids any more, so that it needed the two of them to keep it cranked and loaded. I prowled round the perimeter of the little conversations, attracted by Sylvia's jiffle.

[13]

Her bum moved round to about ten o'clock and then worked anticlockwise to about two-thirty, after which it repeated the gambit. Since she was putting more weight on one leg than on the other, her buttocks were not quite in synch: the left was with Carroll Gibbons, while the right worked on a wilder melody of its own. What a sight! I could feel my pulses getting sludgey. Sod it, I had to have it in tonight – tomorrow, fuck knows what would happen tomorrow! My stomach gave a thin whine at the mere thought of tomorrow ... At least Syl could *move*, unlike Henrietta Crane. Syl was small and rather shifty-looking, but by no means as ancient as The Enigma. Lumps of breast could be seen under a blue dress, although they were unable to coincide entirely with the tit-positions sewn into the dress. Of course, it would be an old dress of her mother's cut down. I'd met Our Syl's mother, but did not let that put me off. I smiled, she smiled, still working the buttocks in friendly fashion. Or perhaps they worked by themselves.

'So you're off then, Horatio?'

'The war's been taking too long. The War Office has sent for me at last.'

'... "I hear your name, and I'm aflame ..." Lushy song! What do you look like in your uniform? Smashing, I bet! All dressed for action!'

'How'd you like to see me in nothing at all?'

'Horatio, what do you mean?'

'Stripped for action!'

'Ooh, we've got a right one here!' she told Ann.

Father was not about, so Mother was being officious for two. She willowed over with a glass in her hand. 'Now, my big soldier boy, you mustn't let Sylvia monopolize you all evening!'

'I only just came over –'

'*Circulate*, dear – And brush you hair back properly, you

[14]

look silly with it hanging over your eyes like that!' These family pleasantries all *sotto voce*.

If she overcame my natural instinct to look like Robert Preston in *Wake Island*, which I had seen five times in the camp cinema, so she had also overcome my father's instinct to have no booze during the evening. '*It only spoils the party.*' No, come on, he didn't really say that; I must have imagined it! But poor old Dad was the sort you could imagine saying it. Fortunately, Mother's sense of occasion had won; she had sucked up to the chap in the post office, who could get you anything, and secured two bottles of pre-war sherry, which she was now doling out gaily, with many a quip about tipsiness, into little bile-green glasses. Mr Jeremy Church, anxious to establish what a merry old turd he was, had brought along a bottle of puce burgundy.

'See you later,' I said over my shoulder to Sylvia, loading the words with all the disgusting sexual innuendo they would take.

I skirted the talk of scarcities and heroism, striving to look by other means than dishevelled hair as if I had just arrived from Wake Island. Collecting a burgundy from Church with a minimum of conversational involvement, I went over to peer down at Henrietta Crane.

The Enigma was offering several items of clothing between blouse and sponge cake – vests, spencers, brassieres, who knows what; wartime conditions gave this sort of girl a magnificent chance to put on every variety of fusty garment her mother had put off fifty years earlier. The sponge cake, notoriously undusted, moved slowly up and down, as if there was someone in it. Yes, I could force myself to get excited. I flung my sexual emotions into gear by imagining spongecakey vulvas. The prick gave a faint lethargic twitch in its sleep, like an ancient dog offered an ancient bone.

Henrietta was sipping the puce burgundy with her mother. They were making faces and whispering together. I perched

on an arm of the sofa beside her – more for the sake of 'A'
Company than anything personal. She moved her elbow
away surreptitiously, so that it could not by any chance
come into contact with my arse.

'So glad you could make it this evening, Henrietta – and
your mother. Didn't have any trouble getting here in the
blackout?'

'So you've just got this forty-eight-hour leave, Horatio,
have you?' That was her mother, not her, looking up
brightly and showing her dentures.

'That's right. Forty-eight hours. The usual.'

'Just two days, in fact.'

I appeared to make quick calculations under my breath
. . . 'Thirty, thirty-three, forty, forty-eight . . .' 'Yes, that's
right, just two days, in fact!' said with as much feigned
astonishment as I dared show.

'And where are you going when you get back to the Army?
It is the Army?'

'First battalion, the Second Royal Mendip Borderers.'

'Well, that is the Army, isn't it? Where are you going to
go?'

'That's a military secret, Mrs Crane, which I am unhappily unable to reveal.' A military secret securely kept
from me, I might have added. While we talked, Henrietta
Crane kept looking at her mother, rather than me, her fat
little lips glistening as she sipped the burgundy. There was
a faint hope that if I waited long enough (say five days) she
might get pissed and shed all her moral standards; if her
moral standards were in proportion to the number of her
underclothes – I was convinced that such a relationship
existed – then the hope was faint indeed, and more than one
bottle of Church's burgundy would be called for.

'Will you be fighting then?' Mrs Crane asked. Her thin
Midland accent made the verb sound the way Southerners
say 'farting', while her tone suggested that, whatever I

was going to do, it was best I did it quietly in a back street.

'Aye, I expect I'll be doing a bit of farting,' I replied.

More in stupor than in anger, I said to Henrietta, 'It's getting stuffy in here with all this fag smoke, and the room starts to stink of beer when it warms up. Would you like to come and see our air-raid shelter out the back?'

The Old Enigma gave me a waxworky look before her eyes slid to mum.

'We've got an air-raid shelter too, you know,' she said, in a tone suggesting she thought she was committing repartee. 'I keep my collection of little vases in there, don't I, mother?'

'That's right, dear.' Smiling at me in elucidation. 'She keeps her collection of little vases in our air-raid shelter.'

'Mmm, I suppose that way they don't get broken if there's an air raid.'

'That's the idea,' Henrietta said. She uttered a short laugh as if it was a prearranged code meaning NO SEX TONIGHT.

'Let me re-fill your glass,' I said. Dog's urine or horse piss?

Ann was still working away at the gramophone, flipping the ten-inches on one after the other. She was swigging sherry with Sylvia and giggling. Jeremy Church was hovering about as if he fancied them both, while Mrs Church listened in agony to the Mole aunt's account of her bombing-out. Most of the records were the sentimental tunes that Ann adored. *How Green Was My Valley, Room 504, Whispering Grass, You Walked By, My Devotion, Yours,* and one that she kept slipping on in my honour, *You Can't Say No to a Soldier.* Christ, she was the only one who had said yes to me; the other bitches here assembled did not even appear to know what the question was!

I evaded old Church, who was anxious to talk about The Agony of the Great War ('You don't remember it but things were very much harder then!'), and commenced to flirt with Sylvia again.

[17]

'You didn't have much luck with Henrietta then!' she said, and she and Ann and I burst out laughing.

Her arms were rather spotty, but we were getting on quite well when I noticed Nelson preparing to slip out with Valerie. He winked at me, a slow thorough wink that must have bruised his eyeball. Dirty bastard! Jealousy seized me. Valerie wasn't bad, a bit hefty owing to her involvement in the Women's Land Army, but very cheerful – and everyone understood that Land Army girls needed it regular; the contact with agriculture made them that way. They would be going to the pub for a pint and afterwards Nelson would get her against our back wall for a knee-trembler. I knew this because he had told me about it in a humble but proud way. He claimed that knee-tremblers were the most exhausting way of having sex. I longed to have a try, longed to be really fucked out.

'Like to come and see our air-raid shelter, Sylvia?'

'What's so special about your air-raid shelter? We've got one too!'

'Ah, but has yours got hot-and-cold running water in it?'

'No, and I bet yours hasn't!'

'It's got a bit of a puddle in one corner! No, look, see, I keep my collection of small vases in there. You'd be interested.'

'You keep your what?'

At that point, when the battle to get Our Syl into a suitable knee-trembling position might have gone either way, enter my father! He had finished his warden's parade, looking for chinks in other people's blackouts. He carried his gas mask and his torch, and was careful not to remove his steel helmet with the letters ARP on it until he was well into the room, so that everyone present was reminded of their duty. The helmet made him look more squat than ever. I noted that its rim barely came up to the most prominent bit of Henrietta Crane.

[18]

His entrance caused some confusion. The old Mole aunt interpreted it as a signal that she should take cover, and had to be restrained by the Moles and Mrs Church from seeing the rest of the war out under our gate-leg table. In annoyance, father pretended he had noticed nothing (a favourite gambit), and went over to twitch severely at our own blackout, pulling the curtains three times, as if signalling to a drove of Dorniers circling overhead. Nelson and his pusher took the chance to sneak away, and I managed to manoeuvre Sylvia as far as the kitchen.

'Let's go out into the back garden and get a breath of air.'

'I'm just going to have a smoke. Do you want a Park Drive?' She offered her packet. 'It's all our local tobacconist has got and I don't care for them all that much.'

'Thanks. Let's smoke them outside. You can't hear yourself talk in there.' Our hands touched as I lit her fag.

'I was enjoying the music. Wouldn't you say Artie Shaw's the best musician there ever was?'

'Look, please let's go out! You can't rely on the music – my mother may stop it at any moment and recite some poetry, if she thinks the thing's getting out of hand. It only needs old Church to get a bit stewed and all hell will break loose in there!'

We were standing one on either side of the kitchen table, puffing our fags, staring at each other. She was looking more attractive all the time. Surely she must have had enough sense to know what I was after? Where was her patriotism? Desperately though I wanted to kiss her – just kiss her if nothing more was available – my whole upbringing prevented my telling her so directly. Everything had to be done according to a deadening set of out-of-date rules, rules so ill-defined that you could never be sure when you were set to move ahead. Or there was the more up-to-date but equally inhibiting way of tackling it, the cinema way, where everything had to be done romantically, where there had to be that look in her eye, and a moon in the sky, and Max Steiner laying on the violins . . . and then you both suddenly went soft and began saying witty tender self-mocking things: 'I've never felt so young before tonight.' 'Why, you're looking positively boyish!' 'It's you, my darling, you bring out the adolescent in me.' 'Aren't we all eternal adolescents!' 'Just for tonight we are!' That sort of American approach was even harder to master than the Ancient British protocol but, once mastered, it gave positive results. The music came on strong, your hands touched, you were over the hump, flowers appeared, you were prone, your lips were touching, pelvic movements started of their own accord. Over our scrubbed kitchen table, nothing began to begin.

'Will you think of me when I'm on Wake Island or some similar hell-spot?'

Then Ann in the next room put on her favourite record, everyone's favourite record, of Len Camber singing *That Lovely Weekend*. We could hear the words in the kitchen, goading me on with their middle-class anguish at war and parting.

> . . . *The ride in the taxi when midnight had flown*
> *And breakfast next morning, just we two alone.*
> *You had to go, time was so short,*
> *We both had so much to say.*
> *Your kit to be packed, your train to be caught –*
> *I'm sorry I cried but I just felt that way . . .*

'I just love this old thing,' Our Syl said. 'There's a chap at the office calls it *That Dirty Weekend*.' She laughed.

'It's a ghastly song – reminds me of what I'm missing. Whipped overseas tomorrow, never to be seen again. Some far corner of a foreign field and all that . . .' By this time, I had an arm round her waist and was smoking heavily against her left flank. She affected not to notice.

'Whereabouts is your brother stationed?'

These days, you'd hit a girl across the chops if she asked you a silly question like that at a time like that. Eventually, I did coax her outside the back door and into the soft dark autumn air. You could tell she wasn't too reluctant. Scrunching the Park Drive underfoot, I got an arm round her neck and muttered a few edifying remarks. I could smell her and she smelt pleasant. The night evidently encouraged her. She dropped the rest of her fag and looked up and smiled at me. She was mysterious, just about visible. A nice face, not a bit shifty. She put her hands up to my cheeks and kept them there.

'I'm sorry you're going,' she said. 'You're nice.'

'Don't worry, I'll be back!'

'I'll miss you when you're gone!'

'Ah, but I've not gone yet, have I? Let me give you something to remember me by!'

We kissed and cuddled in closer. My system started to connect up with hers, going all warm and soft inside, while a fresh young erection nuzzled against her stomach. This was very much better! Sylvia was squeaking and saying 'Oh darling!' in a way that even Ida Lupino would not have despised. Our mouths began to open as we kissed. She clearly had no objection to what she was rubbing against. Scarcely aware of what I was doing, I managed to wedge her in the corner between the garden wall and the air raid shelter where, with a bit of stooping on my part, a knee-trembler should have been perfectly feasible, provided I didn't come my load before I got it in.

Still kissing her, I pulled my fly-buttons undone and lobbed it out. Sylvia knew perfectly well what I was doing. Without any mucking, she grabbed hold of it and squeezed it affectionately while I slid my hand up her skirt. I was just dipping the tips of my fingers into a soft and furry crack when the bloody kitchen door opened behind us.

'Horatio!' My mother in a stage whisper. What timing!

Sylvia let go of my prick as if it had turned into a sea urchin and shrank into the dark. Murder boiled up in my veins. Flipping the sea urchin away, I said 'What do you want?' Good question, really.

I could see her long thin form dimly outlined in the doorway. Father's training was such that she had switched off the kitchen light before opening the door, so as not to spoil the blackout.

'What are you doing out here, Horatio?'

'I'll be in in a minute, mother. For Christ's sake, stop following me about as if I was a kid!'

'I'm not following you! Why should I want to, since you obviously don't want to talk to me, your own mother! Come in at once and look after your guests. They'll think how rude you are not to talk to them.'

'Look, I'm just getting a breath of fresh air. Okay?'

She sounded genuinely angry, and old reflexes of alarm that Sergeant Meadows could never have roused woke in me. 'I know perfectly well that you have Sylvia there with you! Now, come in at once and behave yourself or I'll fetch your father!'

So we went in past her, Sylvia blushing with shame, me a twenty-year-old infantryman, pride of the Royal Mendips, about to die for Old England, erections every night up to my armpits – sometimes you wondered what the fucking hell you were fighting for!

I was so bloody browned off that I stayed on the top of the chest-of-drawers for some while, idly doing a Tarzan act at myself in the mirror. I had so nearly got it in! I sniffed my fingers but even the scent had gone now, bugger it. After another shot at the crucifixion routine, I slid down to the floor head-first and writhed across the carpet. Gradually, with my head hanging brokenly between my shoulders and my tongue lolling, I ascended before the mirror. It was the third day. I was rising again.

I looked really idiotic. Saliva started dripping down on to my sock. I made my cheeks tremble and my forehead go purple.

'Yoooooo are going maaaaaaaad!', I told my reflection, as I twisted one arm under my crutch and the other behind my shaking head. 'Yoooooo. Err. Ger-wing. Blerdy. Ferking. MAAAAAAAAAAAAAD!'

The temporary reversion to idiocy was amazingly refreshing. The Army offered no privacy and it was a treat to go through my old stress-relievers again in solitude. I kept working at the insanity thing until I succeeded in convincing myself that I was indeed going mad. Frightened and satisfied, I undressed and climbed into bed.

Visions of what could have been done to Sylvia assailed me. I'd actually had my fingers in the gorgeous place! 'Come and see me tomorrow, if you have time,' she had whispered; she was willing enough, given time and *That Lovely Weekend*. She had been opening up her legs before the reprise. Those glorious mobile buttocks . . . I felt my old man perking up again at the memory. Oh no, not that! I had to be up early tomorrow morning, and then a long journey before I got back to the depot at Aldershot. Was it never content? It was worse than a baby with the wind, always crying out for attention. What the hell was *wrong* with the bloody thing? In loathing, I put my hand down the bedclothes and felt it. Just to check its pulse, as it were.

It was hot, dry, and stiff, like a corpse stored in an oven, and gorged with blood – all head and neck, a sodding vampire giraffe! Oh God, oh Sylvia! 'Come and see me tomorrow, if you have time!'

The natural law which insures that once you've clutched hold of it you can't let go of it came immediately into force. The thing is your master. The tail wags the dog.

As I started to pacify it by fair means or foul, fantasies crowded in on me. It was next morning. I had woken very

[23]

early, was dressed, climbed out of my window and down over the dining-room bay into the street. Everyone still asleep, only a vanishing milkman in sight. Round to Sylvia's place, up her drainpipe, tap on her window. She comes to window, hot from bed, frowsy, wearing flimsy nightdress, scratching crutch. Opens up, eyes gleam at sight of randy young soldier. He jumps in, embraces her, closes window. On bed immediately. You had to go, the time was so short. Little to say. Fanny swimming with juice, slurps when touched. Marvellous tits, delicious underarms. Roll her over, lovely bum, super expanse of back. She mad for it. Groans in delight. Slip it in from rear . . .

At that point, I remembered Nelson who, probably at that very moment – the moment of reality not dreams – was enjoying another knee-trembler with Valerie against our fence! That's what I should have had with Sylvia if bloody mother had not stuck her nose in! Cancel last fantasy. Instead, open air-raid shelter door, hurry in with her. Lock the door. No interruptions. Syl writhes against me. Lips together, my tongue in her mouth, hand right up, leaning on each other against the damp wall . . .

It's getting pretty urgent. I grab a handkerchief and hop out of bed, still rubbing the vampire giraffe that possesses me. Standing against the bedroom wall, I clench my fists one on top of the other and penetrate them slowly with the gorged head of the beast. A knee-trembler-substitute. This time it's really you, Sylvia, my little beauty. I clutch her buttocks, pull her against me. She's half-fainting with excitement.

Overhead, waves of Dornier bombers are going over, disturbing the fantasy. Heading for Birmingham again, third night in succession, throb-throb-throb. As they come over the chimney-tops, I come over my fists, and stand alone panting in the dark, resting my head against the wall, listening to the bastards fly through the fucking night, on and on.

[24]

No time for Sylvia next morning. Everything hurried and perhaps just as well. With a light tap on the door, Mother came waltzing into my bedroom as in days of yore, before I could even get my eyelids unstuck. She carried a khaki shirt she had ironed. I knew at once she was tearful, even as I sat up hurriedly and looked across the room to see if there were any telltale stains on the wallpaper. The Phantom Wanker Strikes Again! All okay, luckily. Now to avoid her weeping.

'Crikey, it's late! I'd better jump up straight away!'

'Nonsense, darling, you've plenty of time. Your father's come out of the bathroom and there's quite a nip in the air – you'd think it was autumn already. Wasn't old Auntie Mole funny last night? I'm sure she'd had a bit too much to drink! It *was* a lovely party, wasn't it? I – suppose you have no idea where your unit will be going overseas, have you?'

'I told you, nobody ever knows. Sergeant Meadows says it could be Burma!'

'Oh dear, not Burma, I hope! It's such a dreadful place. Don't they call it The White Man's Grave or something? Does your nice Captain Gore-Blakeley think you will be going to Burma?' She sank down on the side of my bed, absently picking up my dressing-gown and fiddling with it. 'I've been a bad mother to you, Horry, dearest!'

'You know that's not true.' But my reply rang as hollow as her statement. She and father had never quite forgiven me for running away from home to live in London, just as I had never forgiven my father for not coming down to find me. All that was four years ago, but memories stay ever fresh in family matters.

'I will write to you, Horry. I hope you'll write to me. I know you're no longer my little boy, but that's how I think of you always in my foolish old heart.' Perhaps it was her way

[25]

of apologizing for stopping me getting it with Sylvia. She took hold of my hand and said, 'Think of your poor loving mother sometimes. You won't have her always, you know, and some day you'll be old and decrepit yourself.'

'Go on with you! You always say that! You're as fit as a fiddle!'

Tears near the surface again. 'I'm not . . . I'm not well at all, really – not that it matters to anyone!' I had a premonition that she would die while I was overseas; or perhaps it was just guilt that made me imagine it. She was startlingly thin – 'a bundle of nerves', as she put it. Ann told me that she often disappeared nowadays, going on her long compulsive walks. Perhaps she would be knocked down and killed by one of the American Army convoys now plunging through the countryside.

We had done this to our parents. We had failed them in some way. We assaulted them just by growing big and strong and sexy while they shrank, year by year, into minor roles, making do with their old clothes and curtains. Ann was talking about joining the ATS – the last of the fledglings to fly, leaving the Stubbs nest not without shrill cries of relief.

All one could do about all this was to be inarticulate. There were tears running down Mother's cheeks. The more she staunched them, the more they flowed. I put an arm round her thin shoulders, a greyhound's shoulders, and her tears came faster. She shuddered and exclaimed between sobs about what a wretched parent she had been. Despite my muttered protests, I was inclined to agree – in those innocent days, I did not realize how rare successful parents were.

'You'll be all right, Mum! Dad'll be here to look after you, and there's all your friends . . .'

'I haven't got any freh-hends! Only you three . . .'

'Well, cheer up, we've knocked the Italians out of the war and the whole business will be over before so long.'

'I'm so afraid you'll get i-hih-hih-hih-hinjured!' She jumped up and ran from the room, as if to dump her grief elsewhere. I gave my bloody kit bag a swift kick as I headed for the bathroom.

More of the same sort of thing occurred in a minor key during breakfast as wincingly we tucked into bacon-and-egg and toast. The gift of speech is a curse on such occasions. Nelson regaled us with an account of the gas course he was on in Edinburgh and Ann essayed a few jokes.

'Did you hear what the British and the Americans said about each other? The British said that there were only three things wrong with the Americans – they were over-sexed, over-paid, and over here!'

'I don't want to hear that word in my house, girl!'

'And the Americans replied that there were only three things wrong with the British – they were under-sexed, under-paid, and under Eisenhower!'

Nelson and I laughed loyally although we had heard it before. We laughed a trifle uneasily: we knew Ann had been out with an American G.I. Probably she had got the joke from him. We hoped she got nothing else – the joke lay painfully close to the truth. The Americans had sex relations; we just had relations.

Clomping about in my boots, I gathered my kit together and rammed my forage cap on to my head so that it clung just above the right ear, its two shining brass buttons hanging over the right eyebrow. I answered repeated enquiries about whether I had packed safely the apples they had given me off our one tree. The time had come to leave. This was it. Farewell, England, home, and beauty! Bus to the station, then away.

'See you in Berlin, mate,' Nelson said, as we shook hands. I kissed Ann and gave her a big hug, wordlessly did the same to mother, who just sobbed and patted my shoulder. We all looked round at each other with pretty ghastly expressions, as I hefted my kit-bag on to my left shoulder. At the front door, we milled about sadly, touching each other. Then I began the walk down the street with father; he was coming as far as the bus stop with me before going on to the bank.

My boots seemed to make an awful row on the pavement. There were only plain, middle-aged women and old men about; no Sylvia. Familiar street, all but empty. Old cars, a dog or two. Mid-August, and a leaf or two blowing in the gutters. Neglect. The fag-ends of old fantasies. There's no way of saying good-bye to people you love; you just turn and look back, carefully so that your forage cap does not fall off, and you grin and wave inanely. You are already separated: a few feet, a few seconds, but enough.

'You'll find it won't be too bad,' Father said, speaking with a wavery jauntiness. The kit-bag dwarfed him as he walked beside me. 'By gosh, if I were a bit younger, I'd be proud to join up myself and be marching beside you.'

'You did your lot last time, Dad.'

'What's that?'

'I said you did your lot last time.'

'All I hope is that they don't send you out to the Far East. It's a horrible place to have to fight a war. Europe's not so bad. The Middle East's not so bad . . . You can get back home from there . . .I don't know what's to become of us all, I'm sure.'

'Let's hope it'll all be over soon.'

'Birmingham got it again last night. You just don't know where it'll all end . . .'

We reached the bus stop. Two old men stood there, not speaking, hands in pockets, staring ahead down the road as if watching for the Wehrmacht. I fell in behind them and Father started to talk about the Great War. Like Mother, he was feeling guilt. He was missing something. He was growing old. As the station bus rolled up, he thrust a five pound note at me, mint from the bank, and said – did he really say, did he really bring himself to say, 'Be a good lad and see you don't go into any brothels', or did I imagine it? I was never sure, my emotions clouded my perceptions.

All I remember is swinging the kit-bag on to the platform of the bus and clutching his hand. Ting-ting went the bell. The bus swept me away from him. He stood where he was, one hand raised in salute, a brave gesture, staring at me. As I stared back, I began to recall all sorts of loving things I meant to say to him only a few seconds previously.

Whatever you may think, Dad, I do love you, even if you never came down to London to look for me. I do love you, and I'll *try* not to go into any brothels . . .

Wartime is much like peacetime; it is just peace brought to a crisis. In wartime, all one's feelings about chance and luck crystallize. Your fate is decided by whether your name falls last on List 'A' or first on List 'B'. You become sure that you are being moved about with intention, but randomly, like a shuffled pack of cards in a conjuror's hands.

In and out of countless uninviting offices, wartime lists were continually on the move. Sure as snipers' bullets, one would eventually break through into reality and settle your hash. It was one such list, a tyrant of the species, which determined that the First Battalion of the 2nd Royal Mendip Borderers (C.O., Lieutenant-Colonel William Swinton), one of the three battalions of 8 Brigade, arrived on the troopship *Ironsides* at Bombay, late in October 1943, to join the other units of the 2nd British Division already in India, to which our brigade had been attached by the courtesy of a yet more despotic list. A subordinate list had determined that I should be present, leaning goggle-eyed over the rail of the *Ironsides*, together with my mates in No. 2 Platoon, listed as one of the three platoons in 'A' Company.

India was a world away from the UK (the pair of initials to which England had now shrunk) and connected with it only by a thin and peevish stream or orders and lists. Bombay was an embodiment of the exotic.

Long before we could see the harbour from our deck of the troopship, we could tell that land lay ahead. The sea transformed itself into many different colours, the blues of the wide ocean giving way to swathes of green, yellow, red, and ochre. A low line of shore materialized. Strange flavours floated on the breeze, pungent, indescribable, setting the short hairs crawling with more than sweat.

As the *Ironsides* moved forward, little trading boats rowed out to meet us, manned by natives intent on getting in their kill first. The boats were loaded with rugs and carpets and brass vases and leather goods of all kinds. Brisk bargaining started as soon as the traders were within earshot, with the wits of *Ironsides* calling down harshly to the brown faces below them. Wally Page and Dusty Miller distinguished themselves as usual. Some of my mates were being jipped before we ever touched land.

For miles round, the sea was punctuated by the thirty vessels of our convoy. We had sailed from Southampton eight weeks ago, with a four-day break in Durban. The hellish *Ironsides* had become our home – so much so that I had developed one of the neuroses that home breeds: desperate till now to get off the hated boat with its hated routines of exercise and housey-housey, I was suddenly reluctant to leave the shelter of a familiar place.

About India, there was nothing familiar. It took your breath away. It swarmed, rippled, stewed, with people. The docks were packed with coolies; as we moved in single lines down the gangplanks, loaded with rifles and gear and respirators and wearing full tropical kit complete with solar topees, we were surrounded by crowds of Indians. NCOs bellowed and struck at them as we formed up smartly into platoons, dripping sweat on to India's soil.

After an hour's wait in the sun, we were marched off through the town to the station, with the regimental band going full blast.

'Heyes front! Bags of bullshit! Show these bloody Wogs they've got the Mendips here!'

It was impossible madness to keep eyes front! We were on an alien world and they didn't want us to see! – it was another example of military insanity!

Leading off the pompous Victorian centre of Bombay were endless warrens – narrow teeming streets packed with animals and amazing vehicles and humanity; though we were instructed not to think of it as humanity but just Wogs.

If I had thought of India at all in more peaceful days, I had regarded it as a place where people were miserable and starved to death; but here was a life that England could never envisage, noisy, unregulated, full of colour and stink, with people in the main laughing and gesticulating in lively fashion.

Knowing absolutely nothing of the culture, caring nothing for it, we saw it all as barbarous. Jungly music blared from many of the ramshackle little shops. Gujerati signs were everywhere. Tangled overhead cables festooned every street. Half-naked beggars paraded on every sidewalk. Over everything lay the heat.

Although I do not remember the details of that dramatic march to the station, I recall clearly my general impression. The impact of noise, light, and smell was great, but took second place; following the long spell on the ship, we were on the look-out first and foremost for women. And there the women were, draped in saris, garments which struck us as not only ugly but form-concealing. Some women paraded with great baskets loaded with cow shit on their heads,

[31]

walking along like queens, while others had jewels stuck in their noses or caste-marks painted on their foreheads. Barbaric! And set in scenes of barbaric disorder!

People were washing and spitting at every street corner, and hump-backed cows were allowed to wander where they would, even into buildings!

'It's sort of a filthy place, is this,' Geordie Wilkinson told me as we fell out at the station. He had the gift of grasping the obvious after everyone else.

On the platform, we became submerged in this motley tide. In the chaos of boarding the train, porters struggled amongst us, grabbing at our kit-bags and luggage so that they could then claim exorbitant fees for their assistance. Their naked urgency, their struggle for work and life, were factors we had never faced before. And the disconcerting thing about the brown faces, when one was close enough to get a good eyeful, was that they looked very similar to English faces! It was the desperation, not the colour, that made them so foreign.

This discovery haunted my days in India. In China or Africa, you are not so weighed down by the same reflection; people there have the goodness to demonstrate their foreignness in every fold of nostril, lip, and eye, whereas the Aryans on the sub-continent – why, that gnarled and emaciated porter trotting along in a small dhoti with your trunk on his head – he looks surprisingly like one of the clerks in father's bank! That snaggle-toothed chap in the comic button-up white suit, arguing in what sounds like gibberish – put him in a proper pinstripe and he'd pass for an Eastbourne estate agent! That bald chap with the heavily pocked cheeks trying to flog you an over-ripe melon – wasn't the corporal in PTC his very spitting image?

I never entirely recovered from the shock of realizing that the English are just pallid and less frenetic Indians.

Our task was at once to defend them from the Japanese

and keep them down, so that their place in the British Empire remained secure.

"If this is bloody India, roll on fucking Dartmoor!', Old Bamber gasped, as we milled along the platform fighting the buggers off. Bamber was an old lag and did not care who knew it – a sour man whose days inside prison gave him a natural advantage in the hurly-burly of 'A' Company.

'Grab us a seat, Stubby!' my mate Wally Page called – like me, he operated a wireless set – as we fought to get into the wooden carriages, struggling against porters and other squaddies.

'Keep a hold on your rifles!' Charley Meadows was yelling. 'Tread on their feet if they get too near for comfort!' It was all right for the sergeant. He had been out here before in peacetime and knew the ropes.

Neither Wally nor I managed to get a seat. Every little compartment was crowded with men and kit right up to the ceiling. It was better where we were, sitting on our kit in the corridor. We collapsed on our kit-bags, puffing and wiping our crimson faces. We sat there for an hour before the train moved out. For all that while, the porters and other beggars besieged us. The most alarming deformities were presented to our eyes: a child with both arms severed at the elbows, beggars ashake with alien palsies, men with blind sockets of gristle turned imploringly to Heaven, skeletal women with foetus-shaped babies at their breasts, scarecrows with mangled fly-specked limbs, deformed countenances, nightmare bodies – all aimed at us with a malign urgency.

'Fuck off! *Jao! Jao*, you bastards, *jao!*', we shouted. We had learnt our first and most important word of Urdu.

'It's like some fucking madhouse!' Geordie said. 'I mean, like, I'd no idea there were places like this here dump.' He was jammed in the corridor with Wally Page and me. We did not realize then how rare corridors were in Indian trains. When Geordie brought out his cigarettes, a dozen

[33]

brown hands uncurled through the window towards the packet. Geordie threw two fags out of the window and shouted to everyone to fuck off. Then we lit up. Geordie was a thin and awkward-looking bod until he played football – where he was often inside right to my right wing – on which occasions he took on a sort of terrible grace, his Adam's apple pumping madly to keep ahead of him. At present you could almost hear his brain wrestling with the concept of India.

Geordie was hatchet-faced, most of his teeth having been removed at the age of sixteen. Wally had a beefy face, a thick neck, and a body like a young bull. The bull-body was covered with yellow hair, less bovine than chick-like; it enclosed Wally from skull to instep as if he had been dipped quickly into scrambled egg. He was apt to punctuate his speech, when chatting to pals, with short jabs to the biceps, as if perpetually testing their amiability.

'We've got a right lot here!' Geordie exclaimed. 'You would think they'd sort of get a bit organized. Why doesn't bloody RSM clear this rabble off the fucking platform?'

'He's running up and down the train like an old tart.' This observation was not entirely true, although certainly RSM Payne was marching from one end of the platform to the other, barking commands with an anxious air. 'He doesn't know whether his arsehole's drilled, bored, or countersunk,' Wally added.

After more delays, and more parading by Payne, the train began to drag itself along the great platform towards freedom. It was late afternoon. A cross-section of the strange world rolled past us. Tea-vendors with urns on their heads, uttering that endless melancholy cry, '*Chaeeeeee wallow, chaeeeeee wallow!*'; the other vendors with their stale buns and withering fruits and fifth-hand copies of *Lilliput* and *Coronet*; the three-legged dogs; the ruffians spitting and pee-ing from squatting positions; the IORs – Indian Other Ranks – below even us, yet apart from their own breed; the

[34]

women washing and drinking at a water tank; the monkeys sitting or squabbling on shed roofs; the aimless people, probing into their crutches for wild life as they watched everything fade under dust; the able-bodied kids running level with our accelerating carriages, paws outstretched, still working on squeezing one last *baksheesh* from us!

This was years before I heard the term 'population explosion'.

The station was tugged away behind us, its people and pungent smells lost. Instead – the maze of Bombay. Its scents! Its temples! Its wicked complacency! Here and there, we caught sight of a face at a window or a family group on a verandah, immobilized by speed. What was it like, what was the essence of life like, in those demented rooms?

From the nearby compartment of our train came a bellow of laughter. Enoch Ford was yelling at us to see what he had found, his doleful pug face wreathed with smiles. 'Here, Stubby, dekko this!' He pointed to an enamel notice affixed inside the sliding door. ' "This compartment is designed to hold eight Indians" . . . And there's bloody twelve of us in here, with all us kit! How do you like that for de-fucking-mocracy?'

Complaints and laughter greeted his remark. But Enoch was a dyed-in-the-wool Communist (by no means the only one in 'A' Company), so his comments were always taken with a pinch of salt. We all commiserated cheerfully with each other on the hells of existence and lit up another round of cigarettes.

The lavatory at the end of the corridor, for which a queue was already forming, caused more fun. It was simply a cupboard, without ventilation, in the floor of which was set a round hole. Through this hole, some light and air was admitted, and one had a fine view of the flashing sleepers below.

'That's your one way of escape from the Army, lads –

down the plughole!' Corporal Ernie Dutt told us good-humouredly. Ernie took everything good-humouredly – you felt in his presence that even India was partly unintentional.

Nameless slimes worked their way down the sides of the bog. Nameless moulds worked their way up. To balance in the squatting position without touching these sides with your hands, while at the same time shitting accurately through the hole, needed flair, given the violent rocking motion of the train. The hole was encrusted with misplaced turds – some of which, when dry enough, rocked their way to freedom unaided.

We left Bombay. The train forged through open country, picking up speed as though desperately concerned to cover the enormous distances now revealed. Villages were dotted here and there – never were we out of sight of one or more villages, with their attendant cattle. In comparison with the city, everywhere looked prosperous and inviting. There were water-buffaloes, tended by infants; some wallowed up to their nostrils in ponds. The landscape kept whirling and whirling away from us without changing its alien pattern, as if a huge circular panorama were being cranked outside the carriage window. We grew tired of the deception and turned to our own horseplay, spinning out anecdotes about home, consuming many cigarettes, repeating jokes about life aboard the *Ironsides*, whose hardships were already becoming humorous in retrospect.

'Crikey,' exclaimed Wally, striking Charlie Cox on the biceps for emphasis. 'Soon as we gets sorted out, I'm going to get myself a black woman! After that boat, I've got a lot of dirty water on my chest.'

'You ain't the only one, cock,' Charlie said. Charlie was our platoon lance-jack. He was in his thirties and going thin on top, but a good man on the Bren gun, sober, thoughtful, and reliable. Charlie had taken awards at Bisley in his time.

We spent a pleasant half-hour describing to each other

how the dirty water had piled up on our chests. During this conversation, darkness came down over India.

We knew and cared little of what lay ahead. Somewhere in the future lay the strong likelihood of action against the invading Japanese in Burma, but first we were due for six weeks' acclimatization course in a mythical place called Kanchapur. We were heading for Kanchapur now; it lay beyond our ken in the onrushing night.

Our talk petered out in grumbles about hunger. The important thing was where the next meal was coming from. We sat unspeaking in corridor and compartment, hunched as comfortably as possible. One or two of us still smoked mechanically. Warm breezes poured through the open windows, stroking the short hairs of my neck. Charley Meadows and Sergeant Gowland of 'B' Company moved slowly down the train, seeing that everyone had their sleeves rolled down against mosquito bites; the battalion was otherwise torpid. As the sergeants reminded us, we had tins of an acid grease to apply to hands and face, in order to keep the mosquitoes away. Despite this, the insects whined about our ears; men began to clout their own faces idly. We considered the possibility of dying of malaria.

'There's more than one sort of malaria and most of them are deadly,' Bamber said. 'Dartmoor's got one of its own what you can die of.'

'Millions of Wogs dies of malaria every year – a bloke told me on the boat,' Wally said.

'Get stuffed, man, them Wogs are immune,' Geordie said. 'They die of it at birth, like, if they're going to get it at all.'

'No, they peg out by the hundred every day. This bloke told me.'

'He was pulling your pisser, Wal. Malaria's no worse than a cold to the Wogs, is it, Bamber?'

'They can pass it on to you or me,' Bamber said grimly.

[37]

The argument faded into the rattle of our progress. We sat on our kit-bags and dozed.

Occasionally, I stared past my reflection at the night, through which an occasional lamp sped. Even the odd point of light spelt an exciting mystery. And as for the scents on the breeze – they could not be analyzed then, just as they have never been forgotten since.

As we drew into Indore, where we were to disembark for Kanchapur, the train filled from end to end with the bellow of non-commissioned voices, cursing, complaining, joking, as we struggled into our harness and sorted out our kit and slung our rifles and heaved up our kit-bags and perhaps smoked a last half-fag – and then jerked and staggered and climbed down to the parched concrete of a station in what was, in those days, the Central Provinces of India.

The lighting was dim except far out on distant sidings. All platforms were crowded with people. Did they live here or did they all take midnight excursions? Heads, shaven or in motley turbans, bobbed all round us, their owners pressing forward in the greatest excitement. Beyond the heads, we gained the impression of a great tumbling city, making itself grimly known by the rattle of trams and hooting of frenzied traffic, and by the glimpses of streets, ramshackle façades, and poor hutches, dissolving into the smokey night. Just the place for a few anti-British riots! Nearer at hand, porters pressed all round us, yelling their weird variant of English. We bellowed back at them, and the NCOs bellowed at us.

'Get fell in! Come on, *move*! move! Put yer bloody knitting away and move! Hold on to yer rifles and get your gear off the train as quick as you like!'

Behind the NCOs moved the figures of our officers, among them our platoon-commander, Gor-Blimey, meaty and as usual aloof from what went on round him.

We got fell in. We became a unit again, a series of platoons formed up along the length of the platform. The porters disappeared. We stood at attention and were given a quick inspection; plenty of stamping, with the train now an empty shell behind us. We marched off the platform in good order, topees high, and transferred our kit to a line of three-tonners standing waiting for us outside the station. All trucks, we understood, were called *gharris* now that we were in India. We climbed into the *gharris* and the tailboards were slammed up after us. Now we were no longer military in appearance, and the salesmen moved in on us again until driven off.

Sergeant Meadows peered into our platoon truck.

'Everyone okay in there?'

'I get travel sick ever so easy, Charley,' Dusty Miller said.

'That's better than having to march, isn't it? Just see you spew up into your topee in proper orderly fashion, that's all. Right now, we've got half-an-hour's ride to the barracks at Kanchapur. There'll be a meal laid on when we get there and then straight to bed, okay? Heads down as soon as possible. It's zero-two hours now. Reveille five-thirty and a run round the block before dawn and it gets too hot to move.'

Groans all round.

'And just remember – you're in a tropical country. No buying any food off of these street-wallahs, understand? That way, you get maggots in your bellies. If I catch any of you trying to buy food off of the street-wallahs, I'll have you up before the C.O. so fast, your feet won't touch. Just watch what the old hands do – like Chalkie White, who's been out here before, same as me – don't panic, remember India isn't Glorious Devon, and you'll be okay. *Thik-hai?* Remember, the Indians are supposed to be on our side.'

Ironical cheers.

'The Indians are supposed to be on our side. They are part of the British Empire and it is our duty to protect them. That's what we're out here for. Never be familiar with one. Treat the Indians with respect and don't let the buggers near your rifles. Never remove your topees in daylight in direct sunlight – sunstroke is a self-inflicted wound and will be punished accordingly.'

We looked down at him in silence. Charley Meadows was a big man with a soft-looking face. His cheeks trembled with earnestness. He feared for us. Much of what he said to us he had said almost every day on the boat; to hear it repeated was pleasurable. It helped to keep us awake.

'What about women, Sarge?' Jackie Tertis asked.

'You're too young to ask such questions, Tertis,' Charley said, and everyone laughed.

The truck-ride lasted over an hour. We swayed in unison as our vehicle bumped along. The convoy wound out of Indore and through a countryside of increasing wildness. The few dust-coated villages we drove through were absolutely desolate. The only life we saw, beyond the odd cow, was an occasional mangy dog, a piyard, glimpsed in the headlights of the following vehicle; it turned its red eyes on us as we passed . . . Every now and again, our *gharri* would surge forward as the driver tried to run one of the dogs over. Hate the place – hate its inhabitants – already the official message was getting through to us!

'I don't think I'm going to go much on India,' Geordie announced. It was even registering on him.

The barracks loomed up, looking as deserted as the villages – except that they were guarded. They consisted of several great blocks, two-storied, with colonnades on the ground floor and wide balconies above. No lights burned, except in the mess hall, where grumpy cooks served us a meal of bully beef hash, plums and custard, and tea. As quickly as possible – and that meant pretty fast – we ate, scrambled for beds, and got our heads down.

We had our run next morning at five-thirty, as promised. The sky cracked at the edge, horizontal beams of light burnished our hairy legs. It was another military day: the country was different, the orders were familiar.

After breakfast, we were paraded for the local C.O. to address us. He was a heavy man, with that air of authority which confers anonymity on senior officers. You could tell he wasn't a Mendip, just by looking at him. We stood on the drill square, rigid in K.D. and topees, listening to the tale of how this was a soft station at which we were to get acclimatized before proceeding first to jungle-training and then to the real business of driving the Jap out of Burma.

'I know the reputation Burma has in the UK, and it is a bad reputation. Don't be misled by it. You will soon discover how the Chindits, together with other units of the British Army, are pressing the war home against the Japanese even now. We've learnt by previous mistakes. The Jap is not invincible and we are going to send him home with his tail between his legs. Burma – most of it anyway – is ideal fighting country for infantry.' A murmur in the ranks, at which the C.O. grew slightly more rigid.

'I repeat – ideal fighting country! That's where British 2 Div comes in. You will be fighting in Burma, make no mistake about that. Over the next few weeks, you are going to be turned into ideal fighting machines. I know you have courage already – our job is to see you leave for the front with fitness also on your side.

'In that connection, I would advise you to drink very little alcohol and plenty of water. Drink your water with salt in, as much as you can take. Also, keep away from local women, all of whom have the pox. You may be offered women down in the bazaar. Refuse them. Don't be misled. They will have the pox, so stay away from them. It's a hot climate, so keep yourselves morally pure. That's all.'

We dismissed.

Many of the bods wandered back to the barrack-room muttering to themselves, dazedly, 'Morally fucking pure . . . What does he think we are . . .'

In the afternoon, we paraded at the quarter-master's stores for new kit. All the kit with which we had been equipped before leaving Blighty had to be turned in. That included our K.D., our respirators, and the hated solar topees. In exchange, we were fitted out with drab green jungle-dress, in sizes that fitted us to some extent. We also acquired steel helmets and bush hats. The latter made us look like Aussies; we swaggered about in them, calling each other 'cobber' and 'me old darlin' ', but it was the C.O.'s speech of the morning which really preoccupied us.

'Are there really a lot of women in the bazaar, corp?' Wally Page asked the store corporal, as we collected mosquito nets.

The corporal paused and looked at Wally suspiciously. 'What do you mean, are there a lot of women in the bazaar?'

'What I say – are there a lot of women in the bazaar?'

The corporal was a thin, sandy, faded man, all rounded surfaces, as if he had spent his life in a pullover two sizes too small for him – a man designed by nature for the fusty dark-ness of the Q.M. stores. We had heard him addressed as Norm. Removing a stub of cigarette from his mouth with thumb and forefinger, he looked Wally and me over con-temptuously and said, 'You young *admis* want to get a bit of service in! You're fresh from the Blight, aren't you?'

'I was in France in 1940 – where were you?' I asked.

'I don't want none of *your* lip! You want to get some Indian service in, that's what counts. We don't call them women out here, *malum*? We call them *bibis*, black *bibis*. That's

Urdu, that is. You lot want to *bolo* the *bhat* a *thora*, you do!'

We had already noticed the convention: as many Urdu words were to be crammed into the conversation as possible. It was as effective as a display of medals for dismaying young upstarts like us.

Sticking to his original point, Wally gave me a blow on the upper arm and said, 'The Corp ain't going to let on about what these black *bibis* are like, Stubby, is he? P'raps he don't know much about them!'

'They'll give you a fucking dose of V.D., mate, that's what they'll do, if you go mucking about with them just like what the C.O. warned you about,' Norm said, pointing his cigarette stub at us in order to emphasize the horror of it. 'You want to stay away from *bibis* unless you want your old man dropping off!'

'What are we supposed to do? They can't *all* have V.D., can they?'

'You want to stay away from the lot of them! Stick to the old five-fingered widow! Stick to the old five-fingered widow and you won't go far wrong.' He banged a pair of trousers down on the counter for emphasis. 'Now then, you young lads, who's next? *Jhaldi jao!* I ain't got all day!'

Wally and I loped into the blinding sunshine, carrying our kit, momentarily silenced by Norm's arid philosophy. We soon found it to be the prevalent philosophy at Kanchapur: hardly surprisingly, for it was only a distortion of, rather than a departure from, the philosophy prevailing at home. There, too, the older tried to impose on the younger the idea that going with women was to court disaster, as my mother was living witness. Even the C.O.'s impossible idea about keeping ourselves morally pure struck me as less unpleasant than Norm's advice about the five-fingered widow.

The awful thing was that Norm's philosophy prevailed. The five-fingered widow was my own constant companion. Never a day went by but a marriage was arranged.

Even on the *Ironsides* . . . But it had been harder and taken longer to come your load on the boat. On the boat, bromide was put in the tea. So the rumour maintained, and so I believed. Something had to account for the acrid flavour of the *char*. The bromide damped down desire – you really had to work to get a hard on, whereas before it always flipped up naturally. Now we were ashore again and back to un-doctored tea, and all the lusts were free to caper once more.

At Kanchapur, everything caused lusts to caper madly. The giddiest dances were brought on by the climate: the heat of the day, the warmth of the night, the voluptuousness of the breezes, the energy stored in everything we touched, stone or tree. The mystery of all we saw in those first weeks in India was also aphrodisiac: the secrets of the swarming people of the Central Provinces, the sense of being nearer than ever before to the basics of life – birth, death, fathering – and the attractions of the *bibis* in the bazaar, where smooth young smiling faces, gleaming raven hair, and perfect shining teeth gave the lie to the filth talked in the Q.M.'s stores.

As the days went by, the original impression that India was beyond comprehension disappeared. It could be comprehended – by its own standards. You obviously had to yield to it, as to sex.

The shithouse at the barracks was cleaned and emptied by a group of Untouchables, who bent low to their sweeping and touched their foreheads as you entered. In there, behind the stable-like door of one compartment or another, I went to a regular evening rendezvous with my dry-mouthed widow.

The rumour was that the Untouchables would bring you a *bibi* if you asked. You just had to say, '*Bibi hai?*', and one would become available. But the association with shit and disease was so marked here that I never dared ask. I fantasized instead. The mere image of lifting up a sari, exploring amid its dark forbidden areas – while those white teeth

[44]

smiled! – and shafting the girl up against the whitewashed back wall of the bog – a knee-trembler in the sunset! – was always enough to send your hand into a frenzy of imitation matrimony.

Those desperate wanks! It was a case of remaining mortally sane, not morally pure. It was never enough merely to lower your trousers – they had to come off, and ankle-putees and all, so that you could crouch there naked but for your shirt, frantically rubbing your shaft, as if by this nakedness you got a little nearer to the real world and further from your own useless dreams. And to see the spunk spattering down into the throat of that lime-odorous pit was never satisfaction enough. Again I would wrench at my prick, red and swollen, until it spat out some of my longings a second time.

Sometimes these sessions ended in disgust, sometimes in a blessed feeling of relief. It was hateful doing it in the shitter, but nowhere else was private enough, not even your creaking *charpoy*, the rope beds on which we slept. As you crossed the sandy distance between barracks and shithouse, with your intention working in your mind, you could see the empty country beyond, tawny by day, blue by evening, and, as dark moved in, lit furtively all round the horizon by flickers of lightning. That world of freedom out there! The hand was a poor but essential substitute for it.

Kanchapur was only a small town. Perhaps it thrived, although to a squaddie's eyes it wilted. The highroad from the barracks led straight to it, so that a sermon on the contrast between military order and the disarray of Indian life was readily available. We walked down from an outpost of England and civilization into a world where grotesque trees and monster insects dominated poor streets; and on

[45]

those streets, tumbledown houses and shops had been built over reeking ditches.

Everything was terrible to us because it was strange. We laughed and pointed in horror at anything you would find in different form in Exeter or Bradford. The bright posters for native films, ointments, or magazines; the amazing script which flowed over shops and placards like a renegade parasitic plant; the unlikely beobabs and deodars that shaded the road; and particularly the smells and foreign tongues and wailing musics – all so closely related that they might have poured from one steaming orifice – these things seemed like the stigmata of some sleezy and probably malevolent god.

Desperately randy as ever, I tried to discuss this supernatural feeling with Geordie, when he and Wally and I were down in the bazaar one evening.

'They've never been Christian here, that's the trouble,' Geordie said, piously. 'I mean, like, they don't go to church proper or sing hymns the way we do.'

'No more do you, you hypocritical fuck-pig!'

'Oh, aye, I know what you mean, like, but I mean I *could* go, like, if I wanted. Anyroad, I've got an Uncle and Auntie what goes to the Baptists every week. Or most weeks, least-wise.'

'These Wogs've got a church down the road here, though.'

'No, I know, aye, yes, they have that, but it must have come too late, like, I mean they've been worshipping monkeys and all that, haven't they, for millions of years. You know what I mean. That's why you've got to be so careful with them. Folks at home just wouldn't believe what goes on here, would they?'

'I wish I knew what goes on here. Don't you reckon the women must be like bloody wild animals in bed?'

'They say the longer you've been out here the whiter they look. I saw a little one just now I wouldn't sort of mind having a go at . . .'

[46]

'I heard that one of their gods has got a dozen cocks!'
Geordie laughed. 'I bet Jack Aylmer told you that.'

'Stop talking shit and come and have a *shafti* at this stall,'
Wally called. Mention of any god annoyed him; he was a
fervent atheist. Wally came from Dagenham, where he was
a car-worker like his father, and we gathered that if God ever
had the cheek to enter the factory, every manjack would have
downed tools at once and walked out on strike.

'Why don't you pack in ordering us about, Wally?' I
asked, but Geordie was already on the move, in his sub-
missive way.

Geordie and I made our way over a plank bridge spanning
an open sewer to see what Wally was up to. He was standing
in front of a wooden stall decked with magazines and
pictures, mostly sugary ones of Indian film stars. Behind the
little counter sat the owner, dressed in white and nodding
and smiling at us, indicating his stock with a graciously
inclined hand.

'Hello, young masters, come to see what you are liking
just now to buy very much! Yevery thing all at very
cheapest prices, young masters, for suit the pocket. If you
are looking pretty magazines with photographs of young
ladies in the Yinglish language, I have very plenty what is
to your likings.'

Ignoring him, Wally pointed to some pictures hanging
from the beams of the stall. Each picture portrayed one
fantastic personage. Their bright colours suggested that they
were posters.

'What a bunch of fucking savages!' Wally said. 'You were
talking about their gods – well, there they are, and a right
old bunch they look! You notice this cove don't have no
pictures of Winston Churchill here!'

'You like the pictures, sahib? I hold light for you to make
the close observation. Yeach and yevery one a Hindu god
and lady-god!'

[47]

As we stared, Wally pointed with particular venom at one of the posters. 'Look at this bastard here! What do you make of him, pulling his own guts out by the fucking yard! Wyhyrr, makes you want to spew up!'

He was stabbing his finger at a splendid and terrifying green figure with the face of a monkey. The monkey wore a crown and the elaborate and stiff golden garments of a prince. The garments were undone. The monkey was ripping his body apart from throat to pelvis, revealing a generalized mass of pink and red entrails. His face was distorted by something between pain and ecstasy.

'Christ-on-fucking-crutches!' exclaimed Geordie. 'Them blaspheming bastards! I mean to say, anyroad, it's bloody cruel, like, even in a fucking picture.'

'Yes, yes, very terrible scene,' agreed the stall-keeper, smiling from one to the other of us. 'This is a depiction of Hanuman, young gentlemen, who fought for Rama and also Rama's beautiful wife, the lady Siva. He is also called the Monkey God.'

'He's marvellous in a revolting way,' I said. 'What did he do?'

'Sahib, Hanuman is fighting for the lady Siva when she is keeping by Ravana.' He performed a little sword-play with his hands.

'Who's Ravana when he's at home?'

'Ravana is the King of the Rakshasas.' His smile suggested he did not mind stating the obvious for us.

Geordie burst into laughter. 'Ask a daft question, Stubby, get a daft bloody answer!'

But I was fascinated by the monkey god. I knew how he felt. Wally was furious that I was taking the matter seriously.

'What do *you* fucking care what this monster did? The bloke who painted that ought to be put away for keeps!' He thumped an adjacent picture, which showed an impossibly pink and rounded young lady with curly nostrils, busily balancing on one foot on a green leaf in a bright blue pool. 'Who's the pusher, Johnny?'

'Yes, yes, this lady is Lakshmi, sahib, the lady-god of fortune and also the pleasure of the god Vishnu, according to our religion of Hinduism, sahib. If you like buy one or two picture very cheap?'

'*I* don't want to buy the bloody things, do I? I've got no time for all that rubbish. It's a load of fucking junk, if you ask me.'

'The pictures demonstrate items in our religion, sahib.'

'Well then, that's your look-out, mate, ain't it? Just don't try to convert me to the bloody nonsense, that's all!'

Ganesh, the elephant god, hung there too, with diamonds in his trunk. Wally knocked him and sent him swinging, to show what he felt about Hinduism.

'Come on, Wally, like – I don't think you ought to take the piss out of the poor sod!' Geordie said. 'He's got his living to earn.'

'How much? *Kitna pice ek* picture?' I asked the stall-keeper.

'Gods and lady-gods all one low price, sahib, only five rupee yevery painting. Very lovely things to look upon, in the day or even night-time. Five rupee. No, sir, you young gentlemen now from the barracks, I know – four rupee! For you, four rupee!'

Wilkinson was trying to move Page on, arguing in his vague way. He now tried to move me on as well – not that I had any intention of paying four or five rupees. Seeing us about to move away, across the plank over his well-flavoured ditch, the stall-holder called that he would accept three rupees.

'Tell him to fuck off,' Page said. 'All that sort of thing gives me a pain in the arse. It's downright sinful! Let's go and get something to drink!'

'Yes, let's go and get something to drink,' Geordie said.

'I'll have a drink when I feel like it, and not before. You two piss off if you're so bloody thirsty! Give you one rupee for the monkey god, Johnny!'

The stall-holder came to the plank and bowed his head, regarding me at the same time under his brows. 'You very hard man, sahib, me very poor man with wife to keep and many many *chikos* to give food, and mother also very sick, all about her body. This is real good Indian painting, sir, for to take home to your lady in England.'

'I'm not going home. I'm here to stay. I'll give you one rupee.'

'Come *on*, Stubbs, fuck it – you can buy three beers for one rupee!'

'Aye, tell him to stuff it up his jumper!'

I gave up and yielded to my friends' gentle advice. As I moved across the plank, the stall-keeper followed, one hand out.

'All right, sahib, I take it one rupee. Come, come, you give!'

Page clouted himself on the head several times. 'You don't want that fucking thing, Stubbs! You cunt, come and have a drink! I ain't buying you a beer if you waste your money on that load of old rubbish!'

But I went back across the ditch and waited patiently while Hanuman was rolled up inside a sheet of frail pink paper.

As I came away with it, Wally and Geordie made pantomimes of staggering about in disgust, clutching their throats and vomiting into the ditch.

'Don't bring that horrible thing near me, Stubbs!' Wally said. 'You must have more bollocks than brains! We haven't been out here five minutes and you're going fucking native already. Isn't he, Geordie?'

'Besides, if he'd hung on, he could have got the thing for half a rupee,' Geordie said. 'It's really a terrible country – you have to say it!'

[50]

'Git your loin cloth on, Stubbs, you jungley wallah!'

'I'll fling you into the fucking ditch, Page, along with the other turds, if you don't shut your arse! Let's go and get a bloody beer!'

After a bloody beer, we went to the cinema. Being a garrison town, Kanchapur boasted three cinemas. One, which showed only native films, was Out of Bounds. The other two, the Vaudette and the Luxor, were in bounds and changed their programme every Sunday, Tuesday, and Friday. Wally, Geordie, and I went to the Luxor, sitting among the peanut shells in the front row but one, to wallow in *The Girls He Left Behind* in which – have I remembered aright after all these years? – Alice Faye sang *A Journey to a Star* and *No Love, No Nothin'*.

Later, back in the aimless main street, night hung like Technicolor in the trees. The promptings of lust were on every side. Kanchapur's street lights, infrequent and yellow, were besieged by a confetti of insects. Every shop was open. Soldiers apart, there were not so many people about, yet the impression was of bustle. A man in a dhoti spat a great gob of betel-juice at our feet as we passed.

'Dirty bastards!' Wally said automatically.

We made our way to a restaurant and sat out on the verandah bellowing for a waiter with plenty of fine deep-throated '*Jhaldi jaos*'. We ordered five eggs-and-chips and beer three times. It felt good to be sitting there, chatting idly about the film as we ate, occasionally waving to a friend in the street, and slapping the odd mosquito that settled on our fists.

Geordie set his knife and fork down and leaned back in the wicker chair.

[51]

'Aye, well, that was almost as good as getting stuck up Alice Faye.'

'I'd rather have Ida Lupino.'

'Ida Lu-fucking-pino? Balls, she's got no figure – Alice Faye's lovely, built like a brick shithouse!'

'She's just an old cow. Even you can see that, Geordie!'

While this debate on female standards of beauty was in progress, Wally leant forward and grabbed my rolled-up picture of Hanuman, which was lying on the table.

'Let go of that, you bastard!' I seized him by his curly yellow wrist. He laughed, pulled back, and crunched the cylinder. I hit him in the chest with my left fist.

The next moment, we were on our feet and confronting each other. I was so angry, I hardly took any notice of Geordie, who was shouting feebly at us both to sit down.

'Come outside, you lousy thieving bastard, and I'll teach you to maul other people's property about!'

'You couldn't teach a pig to piss, you ill-tempered bastard! I only wanted to *look* at the fucking thing!'

'What did you screw it up for then, you interfering cunt?'

Wally went all quiet and crouchy, as if he was about to jump on me.

'Don't you call *me* a cunt, you Midland prick, you, or I'll sort you out!'

'You and who else?' I waved a fist in his face.

Waiters were running up, fluttering their hands about us and cooing with alarm. People at other tables were jumping up, and Geordie was trying to get us away. 'For Christ sake, you couple of dumb 'erbs, do you want the fucking Redcaps on us? Pipe down! Pay your bloody money and let's get out of here!'

He picked the battered roll of picture off the floor where Wally had thrown it and, with much ushering and swearing, managed to get me out of the restaurant. Wally had marched out ahead of us. I pushed past him, knocked down Geordie's detaining hand, and hurried away from them into the bazaar. God knows, I was prepared to swallow the old working-class ethic whole if I could, but there were times when it stood revealed in all its shoddy triviality! I could be as stupid as the next bloke, but Wally's stupidity was an invasion of privacy!

Clutching my maligned picture, I walked on, although I could hear Geordie calling to me. My regret was that I had not given Wally a bunch of fives in the mush while I had the chance.

My temper was troubling me, as it had ever since my early school days. The tendency to get involved in fights had already upset my army career. I was sixteen when I left home and went down to London to seek out Virginia Traven, my great love. Without her, I floundered in the war-dazed city. What pavements I trod were nothing to me. All the streets under the sky of 1939 held only frustration and anger.

My pride had not allowed me to return meekly home from London. Had my father ever come down to find me, to collect me, to take me back – yes, then I would gladly have returned, and felt no defeat. But he never came. When I realized that he never was coming, I marched into the Army Recruiting Centre in Leicester Square, lied about my age, and signed on for what was then the traditional 'seven-and-five' – which is to say, seven years' service on the Active List and five on the Reserves.

I was posted to the 2nd Royal Mendips, then in training near Wells and busily covering most of Somerset on foot, stomach, or whatever parts of the body best suited official inclination. When the regiment was shipped over to France in the New Year of 1940, I went with them. There we proceeded to acquaint the countryside round Arras with the stomachs, feet and other organs which had proved so popular in Somerset. To break this routine, I volunteered to go on a radio-operator's course which, I understood, would

take me to Paris. Paris! Gay Paree! The very name evoked
a knowing leer on any soldier's face.

When the fate-deciding list came through, I was not despatched to Paris. I found myself instead in a North-facing
Nissen hut in Prestatyn, on the North Wales coast. The
powers-that-be had discovered that no man could become
proficient in the mysteries of a 19 set unless he had been
exposed to the ice-filled gales that blew in off the grey waters
of Liverpool Bay. While I was undergoing this mixture of
technology and meteorology, my mates in the BEF were
suddenly plunged into heavy defensive fighting in Belgium,
as Hitler's then invincible divisions rolled through the Low
Countries towards France and Paris.

The Mendips were involved in the fighting around
Louvain, as a thousand heavy tanks rolled down on them.
Many of the friends I knew were killed or taken prisoner by
the Germans, while the mangled units retreated to Dunkirk
and the coastal ports as best they could. The bad news
seeped back to Prestatyn. Guilt and betrayal seemed to be
my lot. I got drunk whenever I could afford it, and was
always involved in fights.

At the same time, the death of my friends made me a sort
of hero. I used to claim – the feeblest and worst of jokes –
that France would never have fallen if I had been there to
sort things out. Only movement comforted my confusion and,
in those terrible young summer days when France was col-
lapsing, movement was everywhere in Britain. The steam
trains pulled in and out of stations; evacuees went towards
unknown foster-parents; hands waved; women fluttered
damp handkerchiefs, and were at once forgotten at unknown
destinations. The next day, in another place, you went on
parade with a hangover and a bloody eye.

Having completed my operator's course, I eventually rejoined the unit, then being reformed after Dunkirk. They
were short of trained men, and I was given my first stripe.

We moved up to the wilds of Yorkshire. Desperately hard up for equipment, we exercised over hills and dales, or endured an endless series of assault courses. The war laboured on, and for some unfathomable reason the seasons took turn and turn-about just as in peacetime, and the invasion of Britain never came.

After a year, I got my second stripe – only to be busted back to signaller a month later for fighting with a private, a great stupid Green Howard I came up against in Richmond. More postings, more trains pulling out of dim platforms, more khaki uniforms in country places. I went back up to corporal, was busted again, and for the same reason – I was drunk and got involved in some prickish quarrel. It did not seem to matter. It was then that one of my mates turned my old joke against me – 'You're dead right, Stubby – if you'd been over in Belgium fighting the Jerries, the French would never have given in!'

I couldn't bear having the piss taken out of me. Remote and evil things happened all over the globe; the blackness in Europe spread eastwards and down into the Balkans. People died and cities burned. In England, there was no Gestapo, only broken sleep and patched underclothing, and lorries rolling throughout the barricaded night. I didn't care! War is strange: it throws people all together and yet it isolates them from each other. Behind a uniform you can be very impersonal. Even a knee-trembler is generally a solitary gesture against loneliness.

Now I was sick with loneliness again in Kanchapur. How long, oh Lord, how long to the next knee-trembler?

With the taste of the beer and the quarrel with Wally Page still on my tongue, I walked towards the far end of the town, past a row of drivers, each sitting almost motionless in his frail carriage behind a withered horse. Every carriage burned a dim light, every driver called out to me – lazily, coaxingly, seductively – offering to take me where I wanted to go. I didn't know where I wanted to go. Behind the last tonga, half-hidden by tree-shadow, stood a quiet young man. He now stepped forward quickly to my side, grasping my arm with his warm brown hand. His face was heavily pockmarked and he wore a white shirt hanging over blue shorts. A serious-looking young man. With an air of spiritual enquiry, he asked, 'Why you are walking, sir? You like nice lady for fornication?'

I looked round. Only the tonga-wallahs were within earshot, and they had surely heard it all before.

'Where is this lady?'

'Woh, sir, she right close by! Two street only, very near, very nice place! She lie for you now, sir, very pretty. You can come with me look see, sir – just come look see!' He spread his fingers wide before him, as if to show how open and above-board everything was, her legs included.

'What's she like?' Were we talking about a flesh-and-blood woman?

He could have looked no more serious had he been describing the C.O.'s daughter. 'She very lovely girl, sir, pretty face and hands, and body of fine shape and light colour, very very sweet to see.'

'I bet! What age is she?'

He held my wrist again. 'You come – I take, and if you no like, no bother, doesn't matter one litter bit. I t'ink you will like, sir, you see – very nice girl, same many years as you and entirely no ageing in the parts of the body!'

In this broken language of courtship and the fragrance of the evening was something irresistible. Morally pure, my arse! With my heart hammering as if I were already on the job, I said, 'Okay, just a dekko.'

Of course she would be an old bag . . .

'Once you see, sir, you like! Making you much excitement.'

So I delivered myself up for the first time into the hands of the treacherous Indian. Once he saw that I was his, he wasted no more words, moving back among the trees with a gesture that I was to follow him. As soon as he stopped speaking his mottled English, he seemed much more alien, and I went in constant expectation of a cosh on the head.

I had to pursue him down a side lane between two shops, where it was doubly dark and stinking. Narrow though the lane was, people stood there in the blackness. A man called softly to my man, and was answered. A hand slyly felt me as I passed. Even then, on that negligible venture, I was taken by an impulse to dive deeper into this morass of living, to sink into the warrens of India, to disappear for ever from view of all those who had claims on me.

The side lane curved and led into a back street – a street very different in atmosphere from the main one. The main street had a sort of artificial cantonment order to it. This one was narrower, busier, more foetid, less easy to comprehend. This was the real thing, clamorous. We moved into its streams of people, women gliding, porters proceeding at a slow trot, animals going at their own pace. Nobody took any more notice of me, following my man as in a dream, than they did of the sacred cow ambling among the little stalls or the men on ricketty balconies above us, gobbing betel-juice down into the gutters below. The acrid odours, that whining music, reinforced the lustful images in my head. Surely people like this must be at it all the time!

My young man spoke to a boy. The boy said something quickly and went darting away ahead, through the miscellaneous crowd, running as if a tiger was at his heels. My sense of adventure grew; I imagined knives being sharpened for me.

'Where is this place you're taking me?'

'Very soon we come, sir, very near.'

At a corner, a huge deodar was growing. It was difficult to make out in the night and confusion and conflict of shadows.

[57]

We dived down a side road and from that into a dark, sweet-smelling court. I paused in its black mouth until poor yellow lights gleaming in upper windows allowed me to get my bearings. There was an old tree here, immensely twisted, fainting in the arms of twisted old houses. Silent men were sitting huddled under the tree, smoking – at first I took them for goats, until I made out their cigarette-ends, which glowed intermittently with their breathing.

My young man tenderly clasped my wrist again, perhaps as much feeling my pulse as detaining me.

'Lovely girl, sir, waiting for you here with sundry embraces, just now, sir, in this room close by.'

Again a whispered word with a half-seen stranger, as we stepped between pillars supporting a balcony or a roof, pushed past a stable containing an animal of some kind (I could hear it moving restlessly), and came to a door. In the wall beside the door, a tiny candle burned in a candle-sized alcove. A faded blossom lay beside the candle, while night insects hovered round the flame. The door was slightly open.

'Come in, sir, come in!'

The young man pushed the door wider. I could not make out the interior at all, so dimly was it lit. Hesitating on the threshold, and still being able to hear the movements of the animal we had passed, I imagined at first that I was looking into a stable, with a high wooden partition barring most of the space. There seemed to be no furniture. Two or three people – including a boy who might have been the boy who ran on ahead – were standing waiting in the dimness. One of them called out huskily in an Indian tongue.

As my eyes grew used to the light, I made out a face near the ceiling of the interior, staring down at me through iron-work at the top of the partition. At that moment, one of the people in the shadows lifted up an oil-light, so that the watching face took on detail.

How could I describe it? Even next day, it was like a face

in a dream. Its dark liquid eyes and its mouth, the black hair neatly gathered back, were common property of millions of Hindu girls. Yet the excitement and imagined danger of the circumstances were so intense that I felt at once I knew her character: pitiful, pliable, timid, passionate. Her face was naked to me in the light.

While the light was still brushing shadows of bars across her face, she became an individual for me – my first foreign woman! Was this the girl they had brought me to? Then I loved her. Sex I wanted, but far more than that I wanted love!

It seemed that my young man was having an argument with the people in the room – for it was a room, and the girl was looking down at me between the bannisters of a wooden staircase. In the delay, she and I stared across at each other.

As we stood there, a wash of brilliance swept round the court outside. It picked out the senile old men and the doomed tree, then lost them in shadow again. Pillars, vines, decaying houses, stable – then the beams of light swung and caught me on the threshold of the room. I turned. As I did so, my young man pushed me from behind. I was outside, in the court again, and felt the door slammed behind me. I heard a bolt clatter home. Two M.P.s with truncheons jumped out of their jeep and ran towards me.

It counted in my favour that I made no attempt to escape or struggle. As they escorted me towards the jeep, my only concern was to protect the rolled picture of Hanuman, still clutched in my hand.

Out of Bounds! It was one of those childish phrases that made the Army seem like public school. With their arbitrary rules and the cunning mixture of moral impositions and brute force which constituted authority, the two institutions were much alike: although there was marginally more liberty and less swearing in the Army.

I told the Redcaps that I had not realized I was out of

[59]

bounds. They were openly contemptuous and disbelieving – that was their profession. They demanded to look at Hanuman. I unrolled the poster and let them sneer at it. Even when I said it had only cost me ten annas, they remained disdainful.

My salvation was that I was fresh to India. My knees weren't brown. I had got no service in. Otherwise my feet would not have touched. They would have had my guts for garters. They had it in for me now. If they ever found me in the brothel area again, I would never know what had hit me. I'd be up the creek without a paddle.

After these admonitions, to which I responded by standing more and more rigidly to attention, the M.P.s drove me through town and back to the barrack gate. They studied me in silent commiseration as I climbed out and made my way back past the guardroom towards 'A' Block.

The bastards! Back in the barrack-room, I was too brassed off to speak to anyone, or to do anything more than climb into bed and get my head under my mosquito net. We were off to Burma soon – precious little chance we would have of getting a woman there. We should get ourselves fucking killed and that was all. What right did the Army have to keep me away from that lovely little *bibi* on the stairs?

It was impossible not to conjure up her face, looking like voluptuousness itself between the bars. Under the blankets, my damned thing rose, the quick-couraged M.P.-defier. When I clutched its sturdy shaft and tried to think what it would be like to push it up the imagined vulva of that half-imaginary girl, the necessity for a quick rub overcame me. Each stroke was to be the last but, Christ, what else was there in life? Although I grudged the old five-fingered widow her easy task, there was a certain relief in feeling the blobs of spunk cut a swathe over chest and stomach.

In those days, it was easier to come than think.

Next morning before parade, I stuck the crumpled picture

[60]

of the monkey god on the wall beside the bed, next to the pin-ups of Ida Lupino and Jinx Falkenberg.

'You know, Stubby, mate, I'm sure the old sweats as knows India are dead right about what they say about women, like,' Geordie said after parade, waving his hands and his Adam's apple in distress at having to say something to me I might not like.

'What do they say, Geordie?' He had taken care to get me on one side to speak. Word that the M.P.s had brought me home had evidently seeped through to him.

'Well, you know same as I do – that you can get into trouble, like, if you sort of go with a pusher, like . . .'

'Come on, Geordie, you were telling us down in the bazaar that you saw a bit of crumpet you fancied.'

'Oh, I know, but I didn't really mean *that*. I mean, I wouldn't really . . . I mean, we do seem to have everything in barracks as we could want, don't us, like? I mean, quite apart from all the parading and training. They say there's two games of football a week. Well, two or three, I think the notice said. We can work up a sweat, you know, me on inside right and you like on the wing, just like at Alder-shot . . .'

'Sure, and then guard-duty at night. Oh, it's a full life okay, a great life if you don't weaken. You aren't trying to tell me I ought to keep myself morally pure, are you?'

'No, no, it's hard to explain. You know I don't want to get at you, but you are my mate, after all, Stubby. I just mean that even without pushers around, it's a pretty full life . . .'

Perhaps he ran out of words. Perhaps he saw the look on my face.

'You think I'm a bit of a cunt, Stubby, don't you? Be honest now!'

' 'Course I don't, mucker! . . .'

Poor old Geordie! There was a lot in what he said. Our regimented life was designed to be sufficient in itself. And he hadn't even mentioned our two-day exercises, when we ran and crawled round Central Provinces as we once had round Arras and Somerset . . .

This rigorous existence was not enough. Every situation generates its legends, and our legend was Burma. We were attuned to every word about it, to every whisper that trickled through, just as we were to messages from that other distant country of sexuality.

Burma was hundreds of miles away from Kanchapur. Mandalay was as distant from us as Toronto from Miami or London from Kiev, and the route there lay across mountain chains and enormous rivers; but our ears were turned in that direction. At this time, late in 1943, the Japanese occupied almost all of Burma and were moving towards Assam. They still had the legend of invincibility round them, which the Chindits were only just denting. They were the fearsome yellow tribes who survived in jungles where nobody else could.

Kanchapur had its share of broken-down old men (as they seemed then – I suppose they would be in their mid-thirties) who had come through operations with Wingate, or through 6 Brigade's attack on Akyab earlier in the year. From these men, stories of terror came.

'You don't want to listen to them,' Charley Cox said. 'Now Mountbatten's arrived, things are going to be different out here. The British have never been permanently beaten yet. That's how we won our Empire. Ain't that right, Dusty?'

Miller, who was the platoon funny man, assumed a blasé officer's voice to say, 'You're bally right, Lance-Corporal Cox. We'll give these little yellow bath-tubs what for, eh, what?'

'There's more men out here now to fight the Japs, you see,' Charley explained.

The Fourteenth Army – in which the Mendips found themselves – was gathering strength and preparing to knock the Japs right out of Burma. But a feeling of misgiving persisted. The Russians were beating back the Germans on the Eastern Front, the Americans were beating back the Japs in the Pacific, our own Eighth Army were pushing up Italy – Nelson was with them – and the Italians had chucked it in and come in on our side. The war in Europe looked as if it would be over one day. The war in South-East Asia had hardly begun.

Between the route marches, the football games, the evenings in the canteen, were spaces with which the Army could not cope. In those intervals, whispers of combined operations and landings on the hellish Burmese coast worked in us like yeast.

The other ferment I was able to deal with personally.

It happened that, two or three days after the M.P.s ran me back to barracks, No. 2 Platoon was on riot exercise. As usual, there were rice famines in parts of India, and rioting against the British in some of the big cities, Indore included. Riot exercise was a matter of marching about in Kanchapur, not letting the Wogs into the main street, and so on. We were equipped with pick helves for the purpose.

In the crowd, I saw the quiet young man who had led me to the girl. He was clutching a book under his arm. Either he did not see me or did not recognize me, but I took the sight of him as a guarantee that the girl – possibly his sister – was still available. For the rest of the day I could not stop thinking of her. Oh, she was beautiful! It was so much more than a fuck I wanted! To pour my heart out – my ambitions – my dreams . . . and to hear the dreams of that exotic creature!

I was determined to have it in before we left Kanchapur.

[63]

Neither M.P.s nor Geordie should stop me. That evening, I had a shower, changed into a freshly dhobied suit of jungle greens, and buzzed off down to the bazaar on my own. The sky was purple, with bars of gold at the horizon, and the fruit-bats were stirring in the tallest jacarandas. I headed for where the tonga-wallahs idly waited.

The quiet young man was not on duty yet. Very well, then I would find my own way to my beloved! This time I would make bloody sure the Redcaps did not nab me. I slipped behind the trees and down the side lane, and at once a different awareness overcame me. No longer was I alone and lonely, a mere debased squaddie; my life was the stuff of romance and I walked in exotic and oriental paths to meet my sumptuous love!

There again was that other crowded street, packed with people, filled with delicious smells. Now to find that little back court! And if I didn't, there must be plenty of adventure in other courts, so – so *fecund* was life and circumstance here. Fecund! My God, yes, the place was fecund, so fecund it was impossible to understand how everyone did not respond to it! I thought briefly, with contempt, of the constipated little C.O. with his silly speech about being morally pure. The sod was dead from the balls up!

After only one wrong turning, I found myself standing again in the amazing courtyard, where the twisted tree died against the twisted houses. Which door? Of course, the candle and the flower! The candle burned there within its niche, the blossom was fresh: a white flower lying on its side, without a stem. In an hour, it would be withered.

I knocked on the door. I was almost shitting myself. Perhaps nobody would come. A bolt clanked, the door opened slightly. A grunt within. The door closed again. I stood there. It opened again, again closed. Could they be going to phone the cops? Phone? In this dump!

I had half made up my mind to leave when a *chiko* emerged

[64]

from the door. It was the kid who had run on ahead last time I was here.

'You like lady, Johnny?'

'Yes – the one I saw the other night!'

'Police, Johnny. Many trouble, police come, many hit, all cry!' He went through a pantomime suggesting that the Battle of Bannockburn had been fought on his doorstep.

'The police didn't see me coming here, I promise. Where's the *bibi*?'

'Thirty rupee, Johnny.' He held out his hand.

'Thirty rupee – you're off your fucking head, Johnny! Look, me no pips, no stripes, just BOR, *malum*? Poor man!'

'You rich man! Give thirty rupee, get lady.' He might not speak English as well as his big brother, but he was a tough little sod in argument. Eventually I knocked him down to ten rupees for a short time. Only when he had the notes in his hand did he let me through the door. When we were inside, he bolted it behind us.

Two oil lights were burning on the floor, beside an old man who sat in a ragged turban nursing a hen. A stick lay beside him. Hen and man regarded me with mistrustful eyes as the boy, with a muttered word, took up one of the lamps and moved to the stairs.

I looked about me. What a ruinous place it was! Bare as a barn! A small door at the foot of the stairs had a grill in it. I peered through the grill. I was staring into the interior of a dim-lit shop. Perhaps it was a tailor's of sorts, for bundles of fabrics stood on the stairs, impeding our progress. I looked eagerly ahead, tripping up as I climbed.

The boy led me to a door and stopped.

'Lady in here, Johnny.'

Gently – nervously – I thrust open the door. There was a woman inside, the end of her sari over her head. The lamp, another small wretched thing, stood behind her, so I could only see that she was beckoning me. I grabbed the boy's light and held it up so that its beams fell on the woman's face.

'This isn't her, you little bastard! Who's this old bag?'

It was probably his mother. She was aged and wrinkled, her gesture of welcome a grotesque parody of seductiveness. In a fury of disappointment, I began to bellow at them both. They grew alarmed and screamed at each other.

'Okay, Johnny, I get. You no make shout, police come, many hit, all cry!' He went through a repeat of the Bannockburn massacre.

'You'll fucking cry if you don't get the girl!'

He came back with her along the landing. She was barefoot. She looked fearfully at me, and my anger went at once. Christ, she was young!

The mere sight of her was enough to wake desire in me. How long had it been! Those liquid eyes again! She looked absolutely terrified – indeed, they all did. The old woman was plucking at my clothes and saying something incomprehensible to me which the boy did his best to translate.

'She say, you no fuck, she suck.'

'Look, Johnny, you've got the ten rupees, *thik-hai*? Then piss off, will you, fuck off!'

'No, no, no fuck off, Johnny. This girl she small hole, you understand? Small hole?' He showed me with two fingers. 'She call out, police come, many hit, all cry!' Bannockburn re-fought.

'I'm not going to hurt her!' What sort of a place was this? I grabbed the girl by a fragile arm and pulled her into the room. I slammed the door, yelling to everyone to stay outside. Without any further hesitation, the girl undressed. When she was naked, she saluted me with both hands together and motioned to the bed.

'You first,' I said, gesturing. I could hardly speak. Had she got any hair on it? Her breasts were so small and sweet – the size of mangoes. As I pulled my uniform off, I could feel

[66]

my prick come up and knock against my belly. The heat was stifling in the little room - it was no more than a cupboard; there was no window to it. I began to sweat.

Watching me, the expression of fear still on her face, the girl climbed on to the bed, which was a hard wooden platform with a rug over it. She went on hands and knees and waggled her bum at me as I approached.

'Don't be filthy, you little cow,' I said tenderly, sliding my hand between her thighs. 'I don't want your arse.' I crawled beside her.

In those days, I was so ignorant about positions that I never thought it possible to have intercourse like the animals; I mistakenly assumed that she wanted me up her back passage. So I turned her over and looked at her face. Her cheeks were burning; perhaps she was blushing.

'You're beautiful!' I said. She did not answer, just looked helplessly at me, her lips slightly parted, her hair combed neatly back, and tied so that a tail of it hung over her shoulders, oiled jet black. I stroked her breasts, her hips, and a twinge of anxiety took me in case I shot my bolt before I got in. I slid my arm down into her crotch. Her little twot was burning hot and became juicy as I rubbed it.

She said something in a whisper, sighed, and made one or two little voluptuous movements, as if to herself. The scent of her was delirious. I smelt the coconut oil or whatever it was as she leant forward and rolled the french letter I had brought down the length of my prick.

I had the image of her cunt in my mind – my fingers supplied it – and I longed to gaze on it, but lust was spurring me on. I pressed her back and lay for a moment with my body against her. She was so small and so hot, and the whole atmosphere of her, merged with my dreams and desires – even the intense fantasy-like strangeness of our surroundings – was so overpowering that I did not actually realize that I had slid into her and that we were tangled together fucking until her slight pelvic thrusts made me aware of the fact. That mere awareness – or the blazing heat of her, which ran through and through me – or the sheer delight of clasping a female body – or the joy of getting it in at last – or the blossoming of life itself into cunts and flowers and orifices – was enough to slip me into a spurting world of orgasm.

'Small hole, small hole . . .' I was laughing and gasping. Small but all embracing. She seemed to be laughing too, a strange short sobbing. Oh, that had really been good, she had come as well. We were made for each other!

I lay by her until the boy banged on the door and the girl called out to him.

'You okay, Johnny?'

'*Chibberao*, son, I'll be out when I'm ready!'

But I got up, reluctantly pulling the sodden frenchie off my prick.

I wanted to do it again.

My feelings were all soft – happiness and gratitude.

The girl sat up on the bed, drawing a knee under her chin. She leaned her head back against the wall. The slight sobbing noises still came from her, which seemed rather unnatural – she could not have been *that* emotionally shaken. I looked at her in the half-dark. I had already observed how deep-set were her eyes. Now a trick of the light made her eye-sockets seem almost hollow. One eye gleamed dully. She appeared to be staring stupidly up at the ceiling.

Looking away from her, I began to get dressed. Things were okay as they were. She didn't have to be mentally deficient or sick of a fever or anything. She was just tired, perhaps a bit shy, perhaps vexed with herself that she had no English. She was lovely and I was grateful to her. Shut in this foul dump, anything might happen to you – it was like somewhere out of Victorian London.

'I'm going now, love," I grasped her hot little hand. Could I make some arrangement with her mother whereby

I – no, she was just another *bibi* and I was just another fucking squaddie.

'You were really so beautiful . . .' Less conviction in my voice than I had intended. What a fool I would feel if Wally or the boys heard me talking to a little whore like that! Reality was creeping in. I was sweating like a pig.

She remained on the bed, one hand brushing her forehead. I went out, pushed by the *chicko*, went downstairs past the bundles, past the old fellow still sitting there with his hen, unbolted the door, stood outside in the cooler air. The white blossom by the candle had not withered.

No Redcaps. I chose my way back into bounds again carefully; but for the rest of the evening I avoided my muckers. There was nothing to say to them.

'You never want to listen to rumours. You want to live on a day-to-day basis.' So said Bamber, and said it frequently. 'That's how you gets through time in jug, see – you never listens to rumours and you lives on a day-to-day basis.'

Old Bamber spoke true. That was how we had lived at school; that was how I lived now. Day followed day, at Kanchapur as elsewhere. Never look ahead. Why do so? The lists were circulating; somebody else had command over what happened to you tomorrow.

Such narrowing down of perspectives did not stop rumours circulating. Few of us were as impervious to them as Bamber, for they represented our fears and anxieties in almost concrete form.

'Do you think that 8 Brigade could be posted to Persia next week?', Carter the Farter and I asked Bamber and Chalkie White, the other old sweat of 2 Platoon.

'Anything's possible in this man's army,' Chalkie said. 'If

[69]

we was to be posted to the top of Everest, I wouldn't be surprised.'

'No, honest, Chalkie!'

'You young lads!' Bamber exclaimed in his deep and melancholy voice. 'You run around after rumours like a lot of young tarts! You never want to listen to rumours. We'll go where we are sent when they want to send us, and there ain't nothing you or me can do about it.'

Wise but unsatisfying. The word on Persia sprang up before morning parade, when we were cleaning rifles; by dinner-time, details were emerging. We were going to join up with Russian troops by the Caspian Sea and help them wipe out the rest of the Wehrmacht.

'Persia can't be worse than this fucking place, can it?'

'Roll on the boat that takes me home!'

'Finest sight in the Far East – Bombay from the back end of a boat!'

'Where is fucking Persia, any road?'

Since nobody in the squad was dead certain exactly where Persia was, it was hard to determine whether this news represented a promise of improvement in our condition. But Captain Gore-Blakeley was seen talking gravely to Sergeant Charley Meadows, which suggested that something was brewing. Certainly Persia sounded better than Akyab or Ramree Island, on the dreaded Arakan coast of Burma, looking onto the Bay of Bengal, the part of the world on which previous rumours had centred.

Then, in another day or two, Gore-Blakeley was seen talking to Charley Meadows again, and the Arakan was re-instated as Number One destination. Persia vanished. Combined Ops, some said. Combined Ops, with 2 Div leading the invasion of Burma from the sea. Before Christmas!

'You never want to listen to rumours,' Bamber said.

We had one consultant to whom we could always turn for advice. That was Ali, our *char*-wallah. In mid-morning, during late afternoon, and all evening until lights-out, Ali sat in or patrolled our barrack-block, selling his thin sweet tea at two annas a mug, dispensing his little sweet cakes for four annas each. He would make his last round before ten o'clock, his urn perched on top of his turban, giving out his low cry, 'Lovely cake and *char*, lovely cake and *char*! Last round of the evening, gentlemen, before finish!' Chaps who rolled in late would ask, 'Where's Ali?', and fuck and blind if they had missed him. Ali was a landmark.

Ali was respected. He had seen countless new intakes through Kanchapur, and knew how to deal with them. He was regarded as a sharp old bastard. He ran a limited credit system, which is to say that he would occasionally let you have a mug of tea or a cake when you were completely skint, on promise of payment the following Friday pay-day. He never wrote anything down, and could remember countless petty sums. By Thursday, all the boozers would be penniless and stay in barracks, playing pontoon for match-sticks and getting mugs of *char* to be paid for on the following day.

Apart from Ernie Dutt, our corporal, the oldest bod in 2 Platoon was Chalkie White. Chalkie was a real old sweat, with a leathery face and perfectly blancoed equipment and polished boots. He was the goalie of our team. On guard parades, Chalkie always fell out as stick-man. He spoke very quietly and was a deadly shot, like Bamber. Chalkie had been out in India before, way back in 1935; the very first day that 8 Brigade had arrived at Kanchapur, Ali came up to him and humbly demanded five rupees.

It turned out that Ali had been a *char*-wallah, or perhaps just a *char*-wallah's mate, up in Peshawar in 1935. Chalkie had then run up a debt of five rupees. Eight years and many intakes later, Ali lived to collect the cash. He never forgot a debt or a face. Chalkie, of course, paid up like a gent.

This feat of memory on Ali's part raised his stock very high in our company. It also raised Chalkie's stock; he became famous as the only man who had escaped from India without paying his *char*-wallah. To Ali we went for confirmation or denial of all rumours, and for obvious reasons: Ali, mindful of Chalkie's long debt, kept himself informed on all possible troop movements. He did this through the network of sweepers, bearers, and traders who worked in the camp and the company office.

It was Ali who informed us we were going to Belgaum for training in amphibious operations.

This information was greeted with groans, especially from those who had at first thought they heard Belgium mentioned.

'I'm going fucking sick, me, mate,' said Wally Page, rolling his sleeves up his fleecy yellow arms and striking me three inches above the elbow. 'How about you? Belgaum! Bugger that! They aren't getting this boy on any amphibious operations.'

'Perhaps it'll just sort of be for a week or two like,' suggested Geordie. 'A week or two wouldn't be too bad, would it?' He looked anxiously at Wally and me.

'I'd rather go to the Arakan and see a bit of action,' I said.

'Me too, Stubby! We can leave Geordie down in fucking Belgaum. Willie Swinton wants his fucking head looking at!' Willie Swinton was Lieutenant-Colonel William Swinton, Officer Commanding the 2nd Royal Mendip Borderers. 'He's just letting Mountbatten fuck him about. We could have done amphibious ops in bloody Blighty, couldn't we?'

'Not in bloody Belgaum, you couldn't,' Geordie said.

'Shit in it, Geordie! I'm not splashing through mangrove swamps with a wireless set strapped to my back for Willie Swinton or anyone, I tell you straight.'

'Bollocks! You're off your fucking rocker, Page! You'll bloody splash when they say splash, and you know it!'

'You think so? You want to bet?'

But as usual we all splashed when they said splash, the

protesters like Wally as well as the non-protesters like Geordie.

Ali was right. Belgaum, down on the west coast below Bombay, it was – there we were destined to spend Christmas, and many other weary days besides.

We marched out of barracks very early one morning in December, wearing FSMO, with exhortations from the sergeants to show bags of bull as we approached the town. As we went down the road, sturdily singing *The Old Red Bags That Mary Wore*, dawn flooded in behind the Parsee tower of silence. The night clouds were torn apart and despatched, turning from slate to gold as they went, in less time than it would take to rip through a Wagner overture, and then fading to nothing before you could tune up for the next number. There was a sort of thrilling terror in the way the sun struggled up into its sky – you knew what a pasting it was going to give you before it set.

Farewell, Kanchapur! And farewell – but I never knew her hot little name!

All that Prestatyn had ever been as a name of hatred, Belgaum became. There was no other similarity between them.

We were not in Belgaum itself – a sleezy military town which we came to look upon as a comparative haven – but in an area much nearer the coast called Vadikhasundi. Here we lived in tents for two months on a freak stretch of red desert, while all about us were jungle, rivers, creeks, hills, the sea, and the mangrove swamps predicted by Wally Page. Here we could fall off LCTs into five feet of stinking water and attack thorn-covered high ground to our heart's delight. We were often so shagged by the end of the day that we could hardly stagger back to camp.

[73]

'Never mind, lads,' said Charley Meadows, mopping his big red face. 'After this, Burma will be a piece of cake.'

Vadikhasundi was what they called a permanent camp. Others had suffered there before us. There we passed Christmas, singing *I'm Dreaming of a White Mistress* with heavy relish for our own wit. Traces of the other poor buggers who had trained in Vadikhasundi lay in the parade ground, where its red sand was discoloured by patches and streaks of yellow – signifying the site where hundreds of BORs had pretended to swallow the morning mepacrine tablet and instead had ground it underfoot, happily risking malaria in the exercise of their own free will.

The whole place was prehistoric. Centipedes and scorpions cantered about by night, snakes skittered under every stone and the mosquitoes were almost big enough to mate with the blue-bottles which stormed through our latrines. The standing tents in which we lived were ancient and rotten; Jack Aylmer, our all-knowing orderly, claimed they had been left over from the Mesopotamia campaign in the first world war. Our mess was just a big native *basha*, a rattan-screen affair with a roof thatched with palm leaves.

Geordie Wilkinson, Dusty Miller, and I strolled over to this mess for tiffin on the day after Boxing Day, discussing the latest rumour, which was that our training was to be cut short, that we were returning to Kanchapur to pick up stores and M/T, and that we were then going straight across India to join a Burmese invasion force at Madras. A nice juicy rumour to get the teeth into, unlike the food we were offered.

The cooks stood in a row outside their cookhouse – three big fat greasy men. One of them, the biggest and greasiest, a goon called Ron Rusk, was cordially disliked by all for his cheerful cry of 'Get in, pigs, it's all swill!'

They dished us out with a chunk of bread, meat stew, mashed potato, and a mug of scalding *char*. It was only a few yards to walk from the cooks into the mess.

As we strolled along chatting, there was a sudden rush of air and a great bird, flying from behind us, dived between Geordie and me and scooped a double claw-full of the stew out of Geordie's mess-tin, which went skittering out of Geordie's hand along the ground. He jumped back yelling, his Adam's apple bobbing in alarm.

'Fuckin' hell, mate! I've been fuckin' attacked! That's my bloody fuckin' grub, that is! I bloody earnt that grub!'

By now, the shabby bird was alighting on top of the cook-house roof, next to its buddies. The three cooks were roaring with laughter, rolling about behind their counter.

'You're in fucking India now, mate,' one of them said. 'Did you think that was a canary? Haven't you ever seen shite-hawks before?'

'I have,' I told him. 'They're what you put in this fucking stew, aren't they?'

'I don't want any lip from you either,' Rusk told me. 'You want to get your bloody knees brown before you speak to me.'

The universal kite-hawks – universally known as 'shite-hawks' – had been plentiful in Kanchapur; in Vadikhasundi, they were two a penny. Like the fly, the shite-hawk was one of India's essential scavengers, and always advanced as a prime item in the squaddie's oft-repeated proof of India's filthiness.

'Never mind our fucking knees, I want some more stew,' Geordie said, holding his mess-tin out. 'I mean, I've got a legal right, like, to some more.' I saw that the bird had raised two bloody weals on his flesh, stretching from near his elbow right down to the ball of his thumb.

'There's no such thing as rights in this man's army. You've had your ration,' Rusk said, waving a ladle indignantly. 'If you've wasted it, that's your fault, but you aren't getting no more, not from us, you aint!'

'Come on, man! You saw what bloody happened – give

me some more. Please!' For a little while Geordie looked near to tears.

'Piss off, Jack! That's your lot. No double helpings – this ain't the Ritz.'

'Give him some bloody more!' Dusty and I said. 'You stingy buggers; you've got a fucking dixie full of the shit!'

'There's others beside you, you know. You aren't the only buggers in this man's regiment, if you think you are. Now – shove off, will you? *Jao!*'

I looked about me. 'Where's the orderly corporal? Why isn't he here? Come on, Geordie, let's get the orderly corporal! He'll soon sort these cunts out. Their fucking feet won't touch.'

Geordie hesitated. He was not the pugnacious type. But Rusk decided the matter.

'Buzz off and find the orderly dog – he'll tell you same as I do. One man, one ration, that's the rule, and if you're fool enough to give yours to the shite-hawks, that's up to you!'

'What were you trying to do? Tame it?', one of the other cooks asked, and they all laughed, their stomachs shaking. By now, more types were lining up for grub, and we moved off. It was useless to get mixed up with the orderly corporal, who was some clot from 'C' Company.

'I'll fix those bastard cooks,' Geordie said, as we sat down at the tables. It sounded like an empty boast.

'Want a bite of my shite-hawk stew, Geordie?' Dusty asked We all burst out laughing.

It was marvellous being one of the lower classes, with the particular generalized lower-classness of the Army. You could be your own awful self, provided you observed the unwritten rules. All the hypocrisies of home-life dissolved. Above all, you did not have to pretend to be content; in the Army, it went the other way – the ideal was to complain all the time.

Certainly there was always something to tick about. Our maneouvres were pure hell – 'total aggs', as the phrase went. On a nearby foetid lake, we plunged off tethered assault-craft into four feet of muddy water and charged ashore. We ran for miles to attack imaginary machine-gun posts. Through thick jungle we stalked others of our kind acting as Japs. We swung across cables and crawled on our bellies. We made long forced marches at night. We slogged through sea and mangrove swamp. We slept in the open and practised street-fighting in a dummy village. We sweated our guts out. And all the time we grumbled.

We grumbled because this was not the real thing but a stunt laid on by GHQ Delhi; we grumbled because the real thing loomed ahead. We grumbled about the Japs, the war, the Army, the sergeants, the officers, the food, the drink, the climate, the lack of sleep, our feet, everything. I loved every minute of it in retrospect.

Even shitting was fun. The latrines were situated not far from the cookhouse. Wally Page and I were there late one afternoon, balanced with our arses over the pole, crapping into a pit.

'Another bastarding night march tonight,' I said.

'I'm covered with jungle sores. Burma will be heaven after this bloody circus!'

'The wireless set plays hell with your prickly-heat, doesn't it?'

All of India sprawled before us, over low bushes. My trousers were round my ankles. Sweat ran down my chest. You could see a bit of the lake among the dispirited trees. Beyond it rolled the hills. Our turds dropped smack down into the lime-covered mess below. Huge flies zoomed about. The sun was getting low, but even the nights were hot.

Wally reached for a bit of newspaper. 'At least we're

[77]

saving money here. My old man and me are going to leave the factory and open up a fish-and-chip shop when I get home.'

'If you get fucking home!'

'Yeah, *if* I get fucking home.'

All the pretensions had gone. The complexities of middle-class life, designed to hide what one was really hoping, feeling, enjoying, suffering – all bowed to the Army code. The Army code was designed to be so simple that the thickest intellect could grasp it; it could be summed up in a classical five-word apothegm: 'Do what you're fucking told!' with its unspoken rider: 'And get away with what you can'.

We did our night march. Apart from the fact that we should have been asleep, it was wonderful to breathe the night air, so much more alive and mysterious than England's air. We hardly needed a compass to find the next village – you could smell it half-a-mile away.

Gor-Blimey was leading our section during this exercise. I followed behind him, humping the wireless set. We moved into a large stone house set in its own grounds on the edge of the village. It was temporary HQ, and there were already other troops there. I had to stay with the captain and raise Brigade HQ while the other lucky sods settled down for a brief kip.

I sat on a balcony upstairs, passing useless messages. Someone brought us up mugs of tea. India was out there – never silent even at three in the morning. Jackals were yelping and unidentifiable night-birds called.

'Wake up, Stubbs! Get me Dog Five again, will you.'

'Yessir.' Here we go again. 'Hello Dog Five, Hello Dog Five. Report my signals. Teapot to Dog Five, over.'

The faint hiss of static and meaningless things, and then a bored voice I recognized as Handsome Hanson's, coming from perhaps half-a-mile away. 'Hello Teapot, hello Teapot. Receiving you Strength Five, over.'

I handed the microphone to Gor-Blimey. After some frigging about with the pressel-switch until he got things right, he spoke to Blue Spot. I sat staring out into the night.

There was no chance of anything as worthwhile as a good screw that night. Bloody Gor-Blimey had really got his teeth into the role of Teapot and was working it for all he was worth. Not until after five was I allowed to slink into a corner of a room and stretch out on a length of matting. No mosquito net, no chance of removing boots and puttees. The flies woke me at seven-thirty.

There was Gor-Blimey, striding about as fresh as ever, enjoying himself, radiating confidence. He was a solid man with a heavy face and a little button-nose, Eric Gore-Blakeley. His manner was quietly authoritative, though he could bellow like a bull when he judged the occasion called for it. My mother had once set eyes on him from afar and conceived a great admiration for him. In 2 Platoon he was considered to be a bit dodgey.

It was mid-day before I staggered back into our Mesopotamian tent. Wally Page was lying luxuriously on his *charpoy* smoking, his hands clasped behind his neck.

'How long have you been there, you cushy bugger?'

'You want to get some service in, Stubbs! I've been here on my arse the last two hours. Had a shower and got straight on with the *charpoy*-bashing.'

'You're a jammy sod! I'm going to get an hour's kip in before dinner. Old Gor-Blimey kept me on the hop all night – I never got my head down at all.'

'You ought to have made your set go dis, same as I did. You want to use your bloody loaf, Stubbs, or we'll never win this war the way you're carrying on.'

'Shit in it, Page – go and do yourself a mischief!'

'And you! Do you want to get that dirty water off your chest? I know where there's a woman here. Ginger Gascadden told me. Apparently all of No. 1 Platoon's been through her.'

'A woman in this bloody dump? You're going *puggle*, Page, that's your trouble! Too much tropical sun.'

He sat up and appealed to Charley Cox who was slumbering in the end bed. 'Isn't that right, Charley? Didn't Ginger Gascadden say he'd had a woman down by the lake?'

'He said she was a proper smasher,' the lance-corporal volunteered.

Wally laughed. 'Yes, well you wouldn't know much about that, Charley, would you now? You prefer sheep or goats, don't you? Little boys, sheep and goats!'

'Fuck off, Page!'

'Fuck off yourself!'

'Where is this woman, anyhow?' I asked.

Cox told me. 'According to Ginger Gascadden, she turns up at that little ruined *basha* down by the lake every evening, with a Wog with her to collect the money – her husband, I shouldn't wonder.'

As I peeled my puttees off and sank onto the bed, I asked, 'Is she any good, Charley? I wouldn't mind a go.'

'You can't keep away from it, you young lads! They're none of them any good,' Cox said. 'Rotten with syph. Even the bloody ground's rotten with syph here – that's why nothing grows. Take the advice of an old soldier, Stubby-boy, and keep off 'em. Fuck your fist, same as I do, and you're safe. Honeymoon in the hand.'

Wally laughed. 'Yes, but you've got Wankers' Doom, cock, you have! Don't care if I do go blind . . . Mrrhhhh, nothing wrong with me, sergeant, it's just the old Doolally Tap.' Trembling and juddering, rolling his head to one side in imitation of someone in the extremes of deterioration, Wally began to sing:

> *Fifteen years you fucked my daughter,*
> *Now you gone and stopped her water –*
>
> *O, Doolally sah'b! O, Doolally sah'b!*

Cox and I bellowed to him to be quiet, and I crawled under my mosquito net to catch some sleep before dinner. After last parade, I promised myself, I would go down to the lake and see for myself if anything was happening there. Clutching my prick affectionately, I sank into elusive dreams.

After tiffin, I took a stroll which led me to the shores of the lake. I had combed my hair and washed my face and shaken off Geordie, saying I would meet him at the canteen.

In my mind, I saw it all. The girl stayed in the hut and I had to pay the bloke first – a hard financial transaction! My mystery girl had cost me ten rupees; outdoors, it should be cheaper. Once I stepped into the hut, all would be right. Our eyes met. She was beautiful – demure and rather shy, brown and shining, with slender legs and a bracelet round her ankle. Without speaking, we established a sort of rapport. I took her in my arms very gently, we kissed, and I learnt for the first time how to remove a sari. Then we made love outside in the sand, while a silver moon rose over the lake.

But reality was a poor crude thing – no wonder so many refuse to accept it! I grew more nervous as I moved round the lake. The realization dawned on me that there might even be a queue for her. What was that about all of No. 1 Platoon having her? Also, the edges of the lake weren't always too enjoyable. I had to make a long detour round a thicket, and cross over a bed of dried mud in which water buffaloes had left hoof-prints and droppings.

Eventually, I had in view the *basha* Charley Cox had mentioned. It stood under a few ragged trees nearby, where gaunt goats nibbled. By the water's edge, a man squatted, looking ahead at nothing. I had no realization of the lengths to which people could be driven by poverty; all I could think of was Ginger Gascadden's verdict that he was selling his wife. How sinful he looked, squatting there by the water while his wife was being shafted by some dirty big Mendip only a few feet away! What a country this was!

Preoccupied by gloomy thoughts and gloomy lust in equal quantities, I was taken by surprise by a small boy who materialized at my elbow. He was a beautiful child, perhaps ten years old, wearing old khaki pants and a ragged vest, and he said brightly, 'You want fuck girl, Johnny?'

'No.' I didn't know. It was all so ghastly. To take but one point, could I even *do* it, knowing her husband and – her – her son, was this? – were within earshot? How could I face them after? 'No, thanks, no girl.'

He smiled and gestured at my flies. 'You like gobble, Johnny? I give you nice gobble? Two rupee, very lovely, very quick.'

I knew how the monkey god felt, tearing himself apart. Life seemed to be crushed between the grindstones of earth and sky.

'How much the girl?'

'Short time ten rupee, Johnny. If she like you, eight rupee. You come see! My sister. Very pretty lovely girl of pale face.'

He took my hand and I went along the path with him. My impulse was to say to him, 'We don't do this sort of thing in England', but it was not the place for small talk; also, I was burningly curious to see the girl. Just curious. It was such a foul set-up. Perhaps we should have let the Japs take over running the country.

The man at the water's edge rose now and stood still, watching us approach. There was activity at the hut too. A man emerged, ramming a bush hat on to his head, a bulky man in trousers, puttees, and boots, wearing no shirt. I watched eagerly to see if the girl would come out after him.

As the other Mendip and I were about to pass each other, I saw that it was Rusk, the cook. His identity discs were bouncing between his fat hairy breasts. He gave me a dirty grin.

'So you're getting a bit of service in at last, then, Jack, are you? Get in there, it's your birthday! I've warmed her up proper for you!'

As he passed, I could smell his rancid body. The boy was still half-tugging me along. I got almost to the hut, and then I could go no further. The thought of fucking anything after Rusk had been at it was too much for me; I couldn't do it. Lust had fled – I just wanted to go back and take a shower. I did not even want to see the cow.

'No fuck,' I said.

'Gobble, Johnny? Super quick time!' He reached for my flies.

'Fuck off! you little bastard! *Jao!*'

'You fuck off! And fuck off fucking you!' He jumped away, spitting anger, waving his fist at me, backing towards the old man, who still stood motionless at the water's edge. I turned and ran.

The misery of it! Sex was as squalid as everything else here. Directly I was away from the *basha*, the filthy images hovered about my head again like shite-hawks. I had never seen the *bibi*. Of course she was a raddled old whore . . . yet the image of rutting, of depraved acts, of the total degradation that seemed to creak out of the parched soil had me in its grip. A torment of lust overcame me.

How could I relieve it except by wanking? Oh, Virginia! Oh, Christ! And there wasn't even anywhere in this wilderness where you could enjoy a decent sensuous wank – certainly not in the tent or the latrine. Nowhere.

There was the lake. Possessed by a sort of fury, I trotted

along its bank until I was well-concealed from the camp. In the water, I could always pretend I was bathing – there was no law against that! I flung my clothes off and trotted into the water. It was muddy and unpleasant underfoot, so that for a moment I felt squeamish.

Looking down at my cock, I took heart – not that it didn't need more than I could give it. At least I could bash it fervently and privately under water.

The water was slimy but warm. Even when one is hell bent on ejaculation by the shortest possible means, water is not the ideal element for sensuous experiment; it conducts away the heat too fast. Fevered though the pictures were that I drove through my brain, it took a long while, as I lay with just my head above water, to work up any sensation at all. Slowly, slowly, persistence began to win the day.

'That man!'

I looked round. The solid figure of Sergeant Meadows stood on the bank. Hastily, I took a stroke or two of a different kind to make believe I was swimming.

'Hello, sergeant!'

'Stubbs? What do you think you're doing in there, man? Come out here! That water is loaded with all kinds of filthy diseases!'

Instead of pointing out that we had swum through worse waters frequently since coming to Vadikhasundi, I said, feebly, 'It's okay just here, Charley!'

'Get out at once and come here!'

Was there an Army regulation against wanking in public lakes? Dismayed, I jumped up, standing in two feet of water. A hasty look down: swollen, yes, pretty gorged with blood, yes, but not erect. I splashed to dry land. Charley Meadows was not standing by my clothes, so I had no option but to parade naked before him, at the 'shun except for my hands over my cock instead of at my sides.

He scratched his head and looked baffled. 'I can never

[84]

make you out, Stubbs. You are bright enough. You were a sergeant once yourself. Yet you will keep on as if you were immature. What were you playing at in there? Were you trying to drown yourself?'

'No, I was just having a bit of a swim. I didn't get any sleep last night, so I thought a swim might tone me up.'

'Tone you up! In that filthy pond, up to the eyes in buffalo shit! You're a regular, Stubbs, you should know better than that! How do you reckon we're ever going to win this war if responsible blokes like you keep playing the fool?'

'I wasn't playing the fool! I was having a swim. I didn't know I was doing anything wrong.'

He sighed. 'Didn't know you was doing anything wrong! You're in trouble, my lad. I'm taking you up before Captain Gore-Blakeley, right away. Get yourself dressed!'

The captain was orderly officer. As I stood before him, he showered captain's questions at me – questions, Army-style, at once stupid and sarcastic. Not only what was I doing and what did I think I was doing, but had I ever seen anyone else swimming in that filthy pond, did I imagine I had been brought out to India at Army expense just to swim in a filthy pond, had I never heard of tropical diseases, did I know what bilharzia was, I didn't think it was the name of an Indian tradesman, did I, and so on?

When this catechism had reduced me to a red-faced silence, Gor-Blimey and Charley looked at each other.

'Sar'nt!'

'Sar?'

'Put this man on picket duty every night until we leave Vadikhasundi.'

'Sar!'

'Signaller Stubbs, you must learn to have some respect for the dangers of an alien environment. We want to get you to Burma fit and well, not crippled with elephantiasis or something equally unpleasant. Understand?'

[85]

'Wharr!' This syllable, only pronounceable with the body rigid, the chest fully extended and the throat firmly clamped down under the jaw, was uttered towards a point some two feet above Captain Gore-Blakeley's head.

I was marched out of the presence. Outside, Charley said, 'You got off light, Stubby, as well you know. You'd better report to the M.O. in the morning and tell him I sent you. Tell him you were swimming in the buffalo pool.' He eyed me hard and not unsympathetically. 'There's a touch of the tarbrush about you, Stubbs.' Resuming a more formal manner, he drew himself up – a gesture I at once copied – and said, 'Signaller Stubbs, di-hiss-miiiiiss!' Right turn, pause, smartly away, ep ri' ep ri' ep . . .

And to think that all of 1 Platoon had been having it in – and getting away with it!

As I headed over the red desert to find myself a couple of beers at the canteen, I prepared my face and shuffled the facts of what had happened into a story that would help me to emerge creditably from the incident. As matters stood, they did not do me much of a favour. Failed fucker, failed wanker was an inglorious double billing. But, in the Army, everything can be arranged to suit the occasion; the pecking order is so steep, the pecks so frequent, that the truth is never as eagerly received as a story that shows one's superiors in a comic or ridiculous light. The discomfiture of friends has to take second preference to the discomfiture of officers and NCOs. Everyone feeds on fantasy, and my story could be arranged not too fancifully to make me show up better than Charley and Gor-Blimey.

There was still half-an-hour to sunset. Shadows of tall trees stretched across the old marquee tent that housed the BORs' canteen. The canteen had only just opened and there were comparatively few Mendips inside.

An old mate of mine, Di Jones, who had been with me at Prestatyn, was sitting drinking *char* with another Welshman

[86]

from 1 Platoon, Taffy Evans. I bought myself a beer and went over to join them.

'Wotcher, Di! Wotcher, Taff!'

'You're looking proper brassed off, mucker, isn't he, Taffy?'

'Proper *chokka*,' agreed Taffy. 'How many more years you got to serve?'

'Too fucking many. I've just been nicked by Charley Meadows.'

Both men were immediately sympathetic, and Di made a lot of clicking noises like a shorting Morse key. 'Your sergeant's got more balls than brains, if you ask me. What did he nick you for, Stubby?'

'Oh, it's a long story. You wouldn't want to hear it.'

'Here, have a fag, Horry lad, and tell us the worst.' Di brought out a tin of Indian 'Players' and offered me one.

'Thanks, Di, I don't mind if I do . . . Well, I suppose you know that there's a *bibi* down by the lake, charging five chips a time?'

As I spoke, I remembered what serious and chapel-going men these two were, and paused, burying my face in the beer glass.

Di Jones looked grave. 'We heard all about that *bibi* from Ginger Gascadden. You want to stay away from Indian women, Horry, really you do. I know you're a lusty young lad with the fires of creation in your crutch, but you'd do best to stick to the old hand-shandy – wouldn't he, Taff?'

But they exchanged winks. Taffy was agreeing vigorously with Di, advising me to stay married to my fist. 'What happened about the *bibi* anyhow?'

'Oh, I just thought I'd go and have a *shufti* at what was going on – look, let me get another beer. Can I buy you two a round? That bloody *char* does you no good, you know!'

They agreed to drink some beer. While I was up at the counter waiting for it, and gazing round to see the day depart, in ambled Geordie. He always looked lost when he was on his own and the idea was growing in me that one day Geordie was going to be told to piss off and hang about someone else – but on this occasion I felt glad to see him.

I gave him a cheery hail, grabbed a fourth beer, and welcomed him over to our table.

'I bet you've been over with that *bibi*, Geordie, haven't you?'

'Me? No, I wouldn't fancy – you know me better than that, mucker! Anyroad, they've sort of got the Redcaps, like, down there, like, to send her packing before she gives the whole bloody unit a dose of the clap, like. So I was hearing – I don't know if it's true. Did you see her?'

'Horry's just going to tell us,' Di said, almost simultaneously waving impatiently at me to continue and wiping the beer froth from his lips.

'I thought I'd go and have a *shufti* at the *bibi* and, just as I was getting there, I glanced back – and who do I see but our Sergeant Fucking Meadows!'

'Likely he was going to have a basinful himself, I shouldn't wonder,' Di said, grinning. 'They're dead crafty, these sergeants.'

'He was hanging about waiting to catch someone, that's what I reckon. Spying on us! So I didn't let on I'd spotted him, but I thought, "Christ, now I'm in the shit, what do I do now?" I mean, if I'd turned back, I'd have walked right into him. So then I had this bright idea – I thought I'd have him on, just for a lark.'

We all sat there pulling at our fags and swigging beer. The canteen lights came on. Night had arrived. 'Go on,' they said.

I laughed. 'I had this bloody daft idea that I'd pretend I was going to have a swim in the lake.'

They all laughed. 'Didn't I always say as you were round the fucking bend, Horry? Swim in that mucky pond, full of buffalo shit!'

'It's not all that bad, mate – it's pretty clean, by Wog standards. Anyhow, I knew old Charley was watching, so I stripped off –'

'You stripped off into the nude?'

'You know me, Di – shit or bust! I stripped right off, ran along the bank, and dived straight into the fucking *pani*!'

They were incredulous, amused, horrified. They laughed and tried to make me admit I had done no such thing. Taffy Evans called another mate of his over to hear the tale.

'I always said as you was fuckin' *puggle*, mate!' Geordie said, laughing. 'What a right carry-on! I don't know ... What did Meadows do?'

'Well, what could he do? I mean, I was bloody daft in the first place, I admit that. You know me – anything for a laugh. And you should have seen his face! He came stomping along the edge – for a moment I thought he was going to dive in after me, boots and all!'

We were all laughing like drains now.

'So he yells to me, "Is that you, Signaller Stubbs? What the fucking hell are you doing in there?" – as if he'd never seen a man take a swim before. I felt like saying to him, "I'm watching Arsenal play the Spurs", but I just said, "I'm cooling my balls off, serge" – and he had me out of there so fast my feet didn't touch! Straight up to the orderly room!'

They were all laughing and repeating 'Cooling my balls off!', and more blokes were coming over to find what was so funny.

I told the story again, throwing in a comic imitation of Gore-Blakeley. 'I suppose you think typhoid is a make of tea, Signaller Stubbs? Eh, what?'

Everyone was in cordial agreement: Meadows and Gor-Blimey had no sense of humour; I, on the other hand, was a bit of a card who had been victimized. Most of us saw ourselves as cards and victims. More beer was ordered, and other victim–card stories told, amid general laughter. Soon someone was reminiscing gaily about the first time he was on jankers.

Mention of jankers reminded me of picket duty. It was almost time to be getting my kit together. Back to realities, I drained my glass and bid them all farewell. As I was going out of the tent, a pasty face in the corner caught my eye. It was Rusk, sitting with a mate and eating a chicken *butti* which was so firmly clasped in his great mitt that for a moment I thought he was tearing his fist apart with his teeth.

Rusk fixed his greasy eyes on me and made a sign, beckoning me with his whole arm. I gave him the Up Yours signal with two fingers and ducked out of the tent, but he called out and immediately began following me. Outside the circle of light thrown by the tent entrance, I turned and waited for him.

He came towards me truculently, the strands of chicken in the corners of his mouth waving for the last time. His sleeves were still rolled up to his elbows. 'You're asking for trouble, Stubbs, sticking your fucking fingers up at me, you know that?'

'Get your sleeves rolled down, Rusk! How long have you been in? Get some fucking service behind you!'

'Don't you tell me to get some fucking service in, mate! You're going to get a bunch of five if you don't belt up, know that? You're on a charge already, aren't you?'

I moved in closer and said, 'You'll be on a charge if you don't get your sleeves down *ek dum*, you fat shit!'

'Don't you order me about: I've been in too long. Don't you go calling me names! I know a thing or two about you, don't I?'

'What do you know?'

'Come on, you know what I know!'

'What do you fucking know?'

'You know!'

'What?'

'About that *bibi*!'

'What about that *bibi*?'

'Well, you spewed your fucking ring, didn't you?'

'What do you mean?' I could see him grinning sickly in the dark.

'You know what I mean, mate! How'd you like your mates to know that the great right-winger Stubbs chickened out of screwing a *bibi* at the last minute? I watched you! I saw you piss off in the other direction when you thought nobody was looking!'

With my right fist, I hit him hard in the left ribs; with my left fist, I hit him hard in the right. There was less blubber and more solid meat than I had imagined. He grunted hard, swiped at me and missed. When I stepped back, he did not come on.

'Want any more, you fat bastard?' I asked.

'You want to get some fucking service in,' he muttered. With that devastating shot, he turned and disappeared in the direction of the cookhouse.

I stood where I was, knowing that I must move to get on picket in time, trying to collect my emotions. All round me was the living night, ever present. Our characters were no more than outlines scrawled on the ruined wall of India. It didn't matter what you did – as long as you weren't found out. Even then, of what significance could our temporary actions be?

Picket was straightforward enough. The moon shone and the night world was beautiful. Of course the ache for women was worse than ever. Wanking did very little to ease it, although it was pleasurable in its own right. The mystery of India – of which I was acutely aware – positively demanded a mysterious woman with whom one could enact the necessary ritual. That night, I did it to myself standing up against a palm tree, rapidly in case I was discovered. Even

[91]

as the spunk scattered in the dust, my intense vision of warm brown entangling limbs, red lips, and the darker scents of desire vanished; I was left holding a deflating and disappointed prick.

Disillusion was setting in; we called it 'feeling *chokka*'. Our amphibious training was strenuous – and the more strenuous it became, the more pointless it felt, although we had then to learn how pointless it really was. At the end of the first week of February, we thankfully left the camp at Vadikhasundi and returned to Kanchapur. Although we greeted our old haunts with delight, the delight was short-lived.

Out in the wilds, we had accumulated some back pay. This was soon frittered away in the bazaars on night-dresses for girl-friends, leather wallets that immediately disintegrated, and flashy silk scarves that incurred military discipline if worn. Geordie Wilkinson bought a wrist watch which stopped twenty-three hours later, and we never found the twister that flogged it to him. As we became broke, we became disenchanted. The demon sex was left to fight the military worm, and the worm generally conquered. Although the dark eyes and tender hot tits of my mystery girl still beckoned, I dared not defy the M.P.s again. To be caught would mean real trouble this time and, in a peacetime cantonment like Kanchapur, the police had everything organized.

So we endured the routine of parades, drills, games, and booze-ups, and went slowly round the bend. No doubt the lists were circulating. It would be a relief when ours came through, whatever it contained – and it could contain nothing good. Meanwhile, we were powerless.

Only on a crippled personal level was some freedom of action possible. Any fears I had that Ron Rusk might spread a lie about my supposed chicken-heartedness at Vadikhasundi vanished. Those swift blows to his ribs had done him a power of good. Whenever I appeared in line with my mess-tins, Rusk would now grin at me and ask, 'Hello, Stubby, how are you doing?' – or, even more familiarly, 'How's your belly off for spots?'

All the same, it was necessary to protect a bod's reputation. If you've given yourself a role in life, you've got to act it out. Men without women really go about spare, and I felt spare up to my earholes – especially at this time when I was all health, eagerness, and hard-ons – to find I was debarred from the world's great fucking match. So I embroidered a bit on what had happened by the Vadikhasundi lake and invented adventures in the Kanchapur bazaar to match the stories of other people's adventures. Yet funnily enough, I could never bring myself to say a word about the little hot girl I had had. I still felt soft about her.

It suited everybody's purpose, in this sterile waiting period, to lie and to believe other people's lies. Even the war situation encouraged fantasy. Japanese forces in Burma were still growing, and very little was being done about it. 'Vinegar' Joe Stilwell in the north of the country was making a bit of a show with his Chinese troops, yet the Fourteenth Army just seemed to be sitting on its arse, apart from a few skirmishes in the Arakan. We had done our amphibious training, and there was not a man in the unit who had not had his stomach filled with brackish water more than once; so why were we back in Kanchapur, killing time, doing nothing, not going to meet the Japs? What were we meant to be doing?

Naturally we invented lecherous fantasies and 'gripped' at each other. Apart from pontoon, this was how we passed the long evenings in barracks.

One of the leaders of the pontoon school was Corporal Warren, a stringy old fellow who always expressed disgust for our stories. After a particularly filthy one from Ginger Gascadden, Warren waved a finger at him and said, 'You're nothink but a bloody fool, Gas, mucking about with native women. Many's the time I've seen young lads like you go mad because of women!'

'*Young lad*! Belt up, Corp, I'm twenty-fucking-five, got a couple of kids at home!'

'All the more reason for you to watch it. I've seen blokes in hot countries go clean round the oojar because of the perverted practices of native women. When I was stationed in Malta –'

'Don't give us that grip, Warry!' someone called.

'When I was stationed in Malta, in Senglea Barracks in Valetta, there was a bloke there called Hunter as shot himself between the eyes with his rifle because of what a native woman done to him.'

'Christ, what did she do?'

'He had only come out from Blighty a couple of months. This was some Arab bint, I believe. See, these native bits of stuff are brought up different to what we are – you ask Aylmer! Ain't that right, Jack?'

'Arr,' said Aylmer, nodding his head so slightly that we could only think that deep experience had almost conferred immobility on him.

'They're brought up different from what we are,' Warren repeated. 'Japanese girls, for instance, they sleep with the white of an egg up their holes every night till they're married, and they have to lay very still so it don't run out over the blankets.'

'What do they do that for, for fuck's sake?' Wally asked.

'It helps keep the hole fresh, doesn't it?'

'What about this bloke in Malta or wherever it was?'

'I tell you, he shot himself – right between the eyes. This Arab bint got some sort of a hold on him. If they really get a man, they aren't satisfied till they've sucked all the good out of him.'

We were all laughing and saying things like 'Don't care if I do go blind!'

'They will, they'll suck all the good out of you! So my advice to you, Gas, if you ever want to see your kiddies again, is don't get involved. If you want it so bad, you better go to one of these here gobble-wallahs. You know what they are, don't you? There's a *chicko* of about seven or eight as hangs about round the Golden Lion restaurant most nights – he's a lot safer than any women and you don't get involved. It's getting involved that causes the trouble.'

'I'm not putting my fucking dick in anybody's mouth,' Geordie said. 'I've sort of got too much respect for my dick!'

'If you haven't, no one else has, Geordie!' Dusty Miller said. When we all laughed, Geordie went red.

So we dreamed our sordid dreams, or made them up. Guilt had so invaded the situation that everything was distorted. When we got it, we pretended we hadn't; when we didn't get it, we pretended we had.

Many of the Mendips were having it regular. In our squad, Dave Feather, a greying fatherly man, had a proper arrangement. His father kept a cycle shop in Bristol. Feather had a regular appointment in a shack behind Kanchapur's one garage; a woman turned up there with her pimp to meet him every Saturday afternoon. There were rumours that she was somebody important – rumours fed by Feather's way of being very discreet about this arrangement. He neither confirmed nor denied what went on by the garage once a week, and he was not the sort of bloke you pressed.

His oblique attitude, hinting at great things without actually claiming anything, was easy to imitate, doing good service for many who hoped humbly to pass as sexual athletes: for the life-distorting barrack-room ethos, to which all were supposed to conform, demanded that spunk should be shed somehow, anyhow, as often as beer was drunk. Our sergeants had one well used tag-line when they let us knock off fatigues for a ten-minute rest: 'Right, break off for a

smoke! Them as can't smoke go through the motions!' With
sex, the same conformity was expected.

This fantasy-barrier was acknowledged in one or two pet
clichés. That old saw, 'Them as talks most does least' was
frequently bandied about, valued as much for its symmetry
as its wisdom. It overlooked the fact that many of the
brigade's most arrant lechers, who had been known to fuck
anything on four, three, two, one, or – since mangoes have
no legs – no legs, said almost nothing that was not a disordered flow of verbal lust. There was no rule that helped
understanding of anyone's sexual life beyond this: that all
men lied and distorted what they did. The process was often
unthinking, a helpless response to the distortions of the system
in which they grew up and grew old.

Self-aggrandizement was the commonest form of self-
defence.

You always made yourself out better than you were. This
was so commonly acknowledged that any attempt at
reminiscence was immediately attacked. When Corporal
Warren started to say, 'When I was stationed in Malta',
several voices cried 'Grip on!', as if they feared that the
self-inflations which must inevitably follow would somehow
deflate them.

The assumption was that anyone speaking on any occasion
when no checks on the accuracy of his statement were
available would be bound to lie.

This I say with hindsight; at the time, I was just a BOR,
eager not to think or feel. But I enjoyed listening to the
stories Warren, Aylmer, and the other old soldiers told. Lies
I could take – my old love, Virginia, had acclimatized me to
them; it was the truth that came hard.

During this waiting time in Kanchapur, Geordie Wilkinson became pally with old Jack Aylmer, who did orderly
duties and suffered from bad feet. I had taken an interest
in Aylmer long before. Aylmer had one line of a song he sang,

always the same line of the same song, which he left suspended in the air in a melancholy way:

'Could I but see thee stand before me . . .'

This line haunted me. It was a snatch from the Flower Song from *Carmen*, and powerful enough to invest Aylmer with a whole history. I saw him as incredibly old – and indeed he must have been in his late thirties – with an ageing wife whom he loved very much; they lived together in a little cottage in Cornwall, the windows of which caught the spray from the Atlantic in rough water. He had been in some profession, a solicitor perhaps, had failed at it, and now eaked out a living, ably supported by his dear wife, as a market-gardener. The war had parted them and she had gone to live with a draper, but he never forgot her and sang his line of song to her over and over again.

Tickled by this vision of comic pathos, I took to drinking with Aylmer and Geordie in the WVS canteen. Of course, Aylmer's background as it emerged was not at all as I had pictured it. He came of a large family who lived above a hairdresser's shop in the Fulham Road, had worked in a glass factory, and moreover bore a picture of a biplane tattooed on his left buttock.

The attraction about Aylmer was that he was a gripper. He was generally disliked for this quality, and had few friends. No sooner did he begin a sentence 'Back in 1936 –', or 'When the Mendips were in the Near East –' than cries of 'He's gripping again!' would arise to silence him. Geordie and I, however, could tolerate his grips. He blossomed and told us marvellous tales of service life in odd parts of the globe. His self-aggrandizement was subtle, lying less in the stories – which were generally impersonal – than in the unspoken claim to omniscience behind them.

At the time, I had no means of knowing whether the things Aylmer told us were true or not: that on Malta, where the Mendips had been stationed, there was a four-thousand

year-old prehistoric palace where human sacrifices were still
carried out; that Chinese girls made the best mistresses; that
several thousand BORs had deserted from the Army in
India rather than go to Burma and lived hidden lives in the
big cities; that in certain African tribes, the women were
circumcized and had their clitorises removed; that Churchill
got a payment of fifty pounds for every tank that bore his
name; that in the wastelands behind Aden there was a temple
now covered with sand which was full of gold dating from the
time of the Crusades; that a Burmese tribe near Lashio ate a
certain food which was deadly poison and then followed it
down with another equally deadly which neutralized the
first; that the respected Chiang Kai-shek, our Chinese ally,
was a secret Fascist; that some day the Mendips were going
to have to liberate Singapore from the sea approach; that
Hindu mothers wanked off their boy-children to keep them
happy and quiet; that a friend of Aylmer's, a truck-driver,
had been stabbed in his sleep the day after he had knocked
down and killed a sacred cow wandering across the road;
that another friend had died in his sleep when a deadly little
krait, a small snake, slithered into his bed and bit him; that
yet another friend, serving on detachment on the North-
West Frontier, had had his blanket stolen from under him
by the Pathans as he slept; that the Indians had invited
Japan to invade and free them from the British and that
Gandhi was in touch with Hirohito; that there were caves
near Bombay filled with incredible erotic sculptures –
voluptuous women with breasts like melons being fucked all
ways by men and animals – which could so easily drive you
mad that only officers above the rank of captain were allowed
in; that as you sailed into Colombo harbour on a calm day,
you could see an old East Indiaman sunk in clear water at
the entrance to the harbour; that Gandhi liked young girls;
that there were gay parrots flying among the trees in southern
India which had been taught to speak Tamil by the locals;

that the Americans wanted to take over the British Empire;
that a Japanese soldier was issued with half a capful of rice a
day and nothing more; that the Gurkhas were the best
soldiers in the world and must be treated like whites; that
prostitution was regarded as holy in many parts of the world,
including Greece and Persia; that the third largest church
dome in the world was on Malta; that there was a battalion
of Poles serving in India who had walked to Delhi over the
Himalayas from Poland when it was over-run by the Nazis, a
distance of several thousand miles across the worst country in
the world; that Hitler had got syphilis; that most of the past
kings of England had also had syphilis, which accounted for
the king's stutter; that the Pope had caught syphilis from one
of his cardinal's wives; that the Yankee Air Force could not
find its targets at night like the RAF, and so was confined to
daylight raids; that the Italian army took droves of whores
with them wherever they went; that there was a castle in
the Highlands of Ethiopia built entirely from the skulls of
some army massacred there in battle; that when the *Ark
Royal* sank, a powerful British secret weapon went down with
it; that the Americans were preparing a secret weapon that
would blow Berlin off the map; that an octopus will die
immediately if you bite it between the eyes; that near
Mandalay stood a town as big as Brighton built entirely
of pagodas of various sizes; that Malta is all that is left of a
land-bridge between Europe and Africa; that Churchill had
delayed the Second Front in the hope that Hitler would
defeat Russia; that by inserting a sixpence into a woman's
twot you could tell if she had V.D., because the coin would
then turn green; that either Kipling or Noel Coward had
written 'Eskimo Nell'; and many other subjects upon which
I was either totally uninformed or needed enlightenment.

Aylmer was a treasure-house of information and mis-
information, like many another old soldier. I had a feeling
that if I could only remember all that he said, I could master

the entire world picture. He gave me confirmation that the world was as complex as I was beginning to suspect, full of conspiracies and contradictions and irreconcilables.

Yet the other squaddies always shut Aylmer up with their cry of 'Grip on!'

'They just don't want to bloody know,' Geordie said when we discussed the matter. 'They'll never listen to anybody, like. They know fuck all and they want to keep it that way. As long as they sort of stay bloody pig-iggerant, they're *thik-hai*. That's what I reckon, anyroad. . . .'

Geordie was probably right. Part of the Army philosophy was to simplify everything down to basics, from furnishings and food to routine.

'I suppose you don't know anything about the Hindu gods – Hanuman and so on?' I asked Aylmer, when Geordie and I were having a mango ice cream with him one evening in the bazaar.

'I don't know much about it, Stubby. The whole Hindu religion is so involved that you can't make anything of it unless you are actually born a Hindu. Some white professors have gone mad studying the ins-and-outs of it.'

'Even Stubby wouldn't want to go as far as that!', Geordie said, and we laughed.

'Have they got a leading god? There seem to be so many of them.'

'The two leading ones are Siva and Vishnu. Vishnu represents law and order – sort of a provost-marshal. Siva stands for destruction and regeneration.'

'He's the pansy-looking one with the flute?'

'That's supposed to be how he looks sometimes. Sometimes he takes other forms. They can change around as they feel like it.'

'It sounds a funny sort of religion to me, though the one with the flute-thing looks quite nice,' Geordie said. 'I mean to say, are the gods good or bad?'

'They're a mixture. Some gods are good and bad, just like humans, and then there are demons and everything.'

Geordie laughed. 'What a lot of primitive superstition! I mean, you've got to admit, it is sort of fucking primitive!'

'Yeah, it's a bit primitive, because it's been going on like this in India now for ten thousand years or more with no change at all. It's responsible for the caste system, is Hinduism, in the same way the Church of England is responsible for the class system in Blighty, only of course it's worse here. Myself, I think Queen Victoria was wrong to say the British shouldn't meddle with religious beliefs in India. The Wogs are not going to progress, as far as I can see, till the whole *subcheeze* of their religion is swept away.'

'I bet they bloody Japs would sweep it away – I mean, if they invaded India and took it over, like,' Geordie said, his Adam's apple bobbing and his hands waving as he sought to convey a complex idea. 'I mean to say, they wouldn't be like Stubby here, like. He's dotty on them Wog gods, aren't you, Stubby, me old oppo?'

Aylmer had seen the picture of Hanuman above my *charpoy*. I had made a sketch of him, too, and later I had bought a picture of Parvati, the pretty pink wife of Siva, posturing in sugary fashion on a water-lily leaf. Parvati came from the stall-keeper who had sold me the monkey god. Later I bought from him an incarnation of Vishnu as Narasimha, with a lion's face and many arms. These three amazing creatures all stared out at the Mendips from above my bunk, glowing between Jinx Falkenberg and Ida Lupino.

'Stubby draws them, too,' Geordie said. 'You know, copies them, like. I reckon it's bad for him – a fine young lad like him.'

Geordie looked anxiously at me, in case I thought he was taking the micky too hard.

'You're a bit of an artist, are you?' Aylmer said. He had a

small sandy moustache which he pressed into his upper lip now and again.

'It's just to amuse myself.' I felt embarrassed. But personal confession was not in Aylmer's line; he preferred general discourse.

'Although all these Hindu gods are so ancient and uncivilized, the odd thing is that Sigmund Freud, the German who invented psycho-analysis, found that we have all these gods and demons, like, in our own minds.'

'What, Hindu gods?' I exclaimed. 'I'd never heard of any of them till I came to this fucking place.'

'I don't mean literally, you nut, but the things they stand for, good and bad and all the rest. Sin and sex and all that. You know we're supposed to be descended from the same tribe as the Indians, so we have the same basic beliefs, like.'

This was too much even for me. 'Fuck off, Aylmer! You mean to tell me we think the same as these Wogs? Then how is it we don't all go round barefoot at home, spitting betel nut?'

'I've seen kids going round barefoot at home,' Geordie observed. 'You want to come up Jarrow way, you do!'

'Look, I'll explain what I mean,' Aylmer said patiently.

He began to do so, but at that moment, strolling up the street whistling, came Wally Page, Enoch Ford and young Jackie Tertis. We exchanged whistles and insults with them, and then sloped down to join them. They were going to get pissed in the canteen, they said.

'What are you hanging about with Aylmer for?' Wally asked. 'Bloody old know-all!'

The Indians in the restaurant stood anxiously by until we paid the bill and moved off towards barracks. The purple air was as warm as ever; fruit bats circled in the tall jacarandas that lined the road to the barracks. Once I looked back to see where Aylmer was. He was following along behind our group, two or three paces back. Once I heard him utter his only line of song.

'Could I but see thee stand before me. . .'

Two hours later, we were all pretty well slewed – except Aylmer, who had gone to bed. We were laughing and shouting good-night to each other. Geordie was singing *Bless 'Em All.*

This, I thought rosily, this was true comradeship! Even old Geordie was better with a few beers in him. What particularly appealed – though I was far from analysing it that night, and many succeeding ones – was everyone's lack of pretension. At public school, at bloody Branwells, our class instincts were so fierce that we rarely spoke about our home-life; the ban, strong but unspoken, operated particularly against parents, those bringers of Life and Class; they were so firmly tabu that you referred to them – when you were forced to refer to them at all – as My People. As if they were stuffed with formaldehyde and kept in a jar.

With Wally and Enoch and Carter the Farter and the lads, it was otherwise. They revealed crude details about their home-life that thrilled and shocked me. Wally in particular! Wally had actually fucked girls behind the sofa in his own home. His parents were often drunk – his mother had once set light to the net curtain and the house had nearly burnt down. His sister used to let the old man from next door feel her in the outside bog, in exchange for sweets. And his father! – Page senior, from Wally's inconsequential account, was an embodiment of lusty lower-class life, a factory hand who fought people in boozers and at football matches, had shaken his fist at their Member of Parliament, had driven a car over a cliff, and, having been caught by Wally fucking a neighbour's daughter up against the wall of a boozer after closing time, had uttered this immortal piece of advice: 'Don't you 'ang round 'ere sniffing at my crumpet – you're old enough to sniff out your own crumpet!'

This utter abandonment of standards thrilled me. Over our beers, Wally and Enoch were trading tales of girls they had had, in the army and out of it. On this topic, they were true buddies – only on politics did they divide, when Enoch propounded Communism and Wally spoke up for Winston Churchill and the king. Try as I might, I could not bring myself to relate my own sexual chronicles, though I cursed myself for my squeamishness; about Virginia and Esmeralda at least I still felt a great deal of sentiment, and sentiment seemed to be precisely what Wally and Enoch were free from. Their pushers, their bits of skirt, were evidently despatched with amazing aplomb, in an absent-minded succession of blow-throughs. Or so they told it.

Although I admired this freedom from the lame tradition in which I had been brought up – the tradition whereby a girl was supposed to be loaded with chocolates, fair words and moonlight first – I was unable to hide a feeling that these quick fucks here and there had been remarkably perfunctory, not to say brief. The object always seemed to be to come your muck, as Enoch called it, as fast as possible. Once, someone mentioned that the Hindus stretched their love-making out for perhaps an hour at a time.

'Dirty bastards!' Wally said. ' "Whip it in, whip it out, and wipe it", that's my motto.'

The one reservation to my admiration which I would admit at this time was that Wally and Enoch, like many others whose stories I listened to, were apparently com-pletely blind to the look of the girl's face. 'She were an ugly cow, but by Christ she could fuck!', was Enoch's summary of one woman he had had in the factory where he worked. This blindness extended amazingly to an indifference to the woman's body. I often wondered if Wally – or any of the others – had ever contemplated a girl's naked body and been moved by the sight. They seemed to have had so many opportunities and squandered them so recklessly.

For all that, surely quantity was a good substitute for quality? By the time we broke up that evening, Enoch giving his extraordinary whoop of 'Honey pears!', I was once more full of envy of their free way of life.

I wove my way to the shitter, to find that young Jackie Tertis was there before me, his round baby face gleaming with sweat.

'Oooh, I ain't used to so much booze!' he groaned. Next moment, he was spewing all over the floor.

Hopping out of the way, I went to have a long pee, leaning my head wearily against the wall as I let it flow. Bed I wanted.

'Jesus Fucking Christ! I can't take this sodding shitting Wog beer!' Jackie said, after one last heave. 'Makes me spew my ring every time! I wish I was home, that's a fact!'

Tertis was only eighteen, the baby of the platoon.

'They say the first five years are the worst. Buck up, you'll feel better now you've got it off your kidneys!'

'I don't feel better. Blimey, I feel fucking awful!' He looked awful, his face pale and glistening, his hair disordered, and with a fair spatter of sick all down his bushjacket.

'Come on, let's get over to the barracks, get some kip.'

As we crossed the square, he said, recovering a little, 'I didn't used to drink, you know, Stubby. My dad's a teetotaller. He'd be that mad if he could see me now. Me old ma died a couple of years ago and things haven't been the same. I wish I was home!'

'You're better away from home getting your knees brown.'

He sniffed. I wondered if he was going to start weeping. 'It's all right for you – you're a regular. My life's been different from you lot. Shall I tell you something, Stubby?'

'Come on, Tertis, you're pissed, I'm pissed – let's get to fucking kip!'

But he stopped at the bottom of the steps to the barracks. I went up on to the stone verandah. Draggingly, he followed and said, 'I wouldn't tell you this if I wasn't pissed – for

God's sake don't tell Page or the others, but I've never had a girl. Never fucked one, I mean, not in my bloody fornicating life.'

'Ah, fuck off! What about that bird you said you fucked up a lane when you were blackberrying?'

'I had to make something up. I didn't get to fuck her – I had a girl, I mean I've still got her, I think, because we talked about getting married and everything, but I mean we were in bloody love, and I never fucked her. She did let me feel her tits once. I was longing to yark it up her but I didn't dare.'

We stood in the great shade of the building. Distantly, dogs were barking. There was never complete silence: the place was too big for that. The stone under my hand was cool.

'She's got really lovely tits,' Tertis said, with conviction. 'Very firm tits. Oh God, I wish she was fucking here now. I'd fuck her now, I wouldn't hesitate. I'd be right in there!'

'Why didn't you fuck her then?'

'It's different in fucking Blighty, isn't it? Blighty's full of restrictions. I wonder if I'm going to throw up again?'

'You want to stick to the old five-fingered widow.'

'Don't tell me nothing about that!'

'That's what they say.'

The sun was gone and it would be back in strength next morning as sure as eggs were eggs. It sounded as if those fucking piyards had gone mad. It was just wonderful to be warm at ten o'clock at night and watch the lightning flicker pale about the horizon. I sat down on a step and lit up a Wog Players, flipping one to Tertis. Tertis sat clumsily beside me and lit up too.

'You aren't going to spew again, are you?', I asked.

'Hope not.'

A jackal was doing its nut in the distance. That was what had started the dogs off. It had an irritating yip like an insane schoolgirl giggle. You hated bastarding jackals without ever seeing one. A sort of bisexual *thing*, like a Hindu devil, laughing its dick off at the edge of nowhere.

'Stubby, you've fucked one of these *bibis*, haven't you? Wally said you had.'

I inhaled deeply and let the fag smoke whistle out through my teeth.

'Have you ever seen a woman in the nude, Jackie? You know, stark bolluck-naked?'

Leaning towards me in a drunken exaggerated fashion, he said, 'No. I wish I had. The next time you go to a brothel, perhaps I could come along with you – just to fucking see what it's like.'

'It's the most marvellous thing in the world to see a woman bolluck-naked, to have her next to you, to stare at it all and feel it and see her enjoying it.'

'Oh Christ, shut up!'

'Your dick up round your neck . . . They're glad of it too, glad to be seen. They aren't just women, they're human. For all old Wally says, a fuck's hardly a fuck unless you can get 'em naked.'

'Oh Christ, shut up or I'll have to go and wank my fucking self off again. It's this fucking climate. I can't stop myself doing it.'

'You want to keep yourself morally pure, Tertis, like the C.O. said.'

'Come on, don't shit me, Stubby! I have to keep on bashing my bishop – it makes me feel awful. It's twitching in my pants if I just mention its name!'

I stubbed my cigarette against the stone and climbed to my feet. It was an unwritten breach of Army code to air this sort of confidence. We all had troubles – the same troubles.

'You want to sleep with fucking boxing gloves on, mate,' I said, and went in in search of my *charpoy*.

Directly I was under the mosquito net, I was asleep, beer-sodden and careless if not entirely carefree. The next thing I heard was Ernie Dutt bellowing in the morning, in the time-approved manner, 'Wakey-wakey, you lads, out of those stinking wanking-pits at the double!'

That's you, Tertis, you turd, I thought. Sluggishly, I joined in the bunfight that went on before morning parade and inspection.

book 2
The Old Five-Fingered Widow

SCENE: Kanchapur Barracks. Dazzling sunlight. *Private Aylmer* and *Signaller Stubbs*, whitewash brushes in hand, are on fatigues. *Sergeant Meadows* arrives to see how they are progressing.

Sgt M: Come on, come on, you two! Let's see a bit of action!

Stubbs: Action! We aren't likely to see any action in this man's army. I thought we were supposed to be invading the Arakan, Sarge, not bashing these bloody stones!

Aylmer: I expect Delhi have decided it's better strategy for the Japs to come to us than for us to go and meet the Japs.

Sgt M: You'd better hear the latest, then. All the landing-craft in this theatre of war have been withdrawn. Mountbatten did what he could, but the Mediterranean theatre had priority over us, and they've taken the lot.

Stubbs: Poor old Fourteenth Army! Bottom of the list again.

Aylmer: You mean all that training, like, down in Belgaum was for nothing?

Sgt M: All amphibious vehicles have been withdrawn. That's how I heard it.

Stubbs: Jesus Fucking Christ! We might as well pack up and go home!

Sgt M: You'll be lucky! They'll probably send us to Assam instead.

Aylmer: Assam! That's even worse than the Arakan! As you probably know, Charley, Assam is the wettest place on Earth. We can't fight there.

Sgt M: That's up to the Japs, isn't it? If they come in that way, someone's got to stop 'em. Who better than 8 Bde?

Aylmer: There's a place in Assam called Sharapinji where they get over a thousand inches of rain per year. You can't fight in a climate like that!

Sgt M: They'll issue us with umbrellas. Now, get on painting those stones. I want to see that whole lot done before tiffin.

Painting stones, Aylmer and I were the first to get this official confirmation of a rumour that had been circulating ever since we returned to Kanchapur. We had carried out our amphibious training – and there were no longer any landing craft to land in!

Unknown to us, horse-trading had been carried out on the highest level. Stalin, Roosevelt, Churchill, and Chiang Kai-shek had all been involved, at a Teheran conference and after. Step-by-step, amphibious ops in South-East Asia were cancelled, and the fleets involved returned to England or the Mediterranean. The Fourteenth Army was left committed to an overland war. And the 1st Battalion was committed to a further time-defying seven weeks kicking its heels in Kanchapur, while the lists whirled and fluttered above our heads.

Twice a week during this waiting period, we used to play football. We had some good games and while they were in progress there was a feeling that something was happening – or at least you forgot that nothing was happening. At right wing, I was one of our goal-scorers.

When the British first invaded the East, they found to their disgust that the natives were slackers almost to a man and enjoyed no sport except pig-sticking. They introduced among themselves a regime of sport which went on even during a war in which the Japanese sat almost at the gates of India.

No doubt part of the idea was to sublimate the sex urge; if so, it was unsuccessful.

I was showering after one game. The usual horseplay was going on, with plenty of towel-flicking. I hated all the ox-like bodies, and bagged the shower at the end of the row, next to Di Jones, who played outside left. Di was his usual quiet self, even after a game of football; he soaped his armpits with an episcopalian air.

Thrusting his head out of a miniature waterfall, Di asked, 'You don't feel like a bit of a bunk-up this evening, Stubby, by any chance?'

'A bit of what?'

'Dipping your wick, man!'

This was unlike the staid, chapel-going Di I thought I knew. 'I'm careful where I dip my wick, mate. Got a bit of respect for it.'

'So have I for mine.' To be honest, Di had only a tiny stub of dick, and very pale and pointed at that, sticking out like an inch of unlit candle from its mat of hair. 'All the same, I thought I'd give it a bit of an airing like, this evening, along with another mate of mine. I wondered if you'd like to come along. I remember how you got done out of a bunk-up while we was on amphibious ops down in Belgaum.'

'Yeah, well, I've got to do my blancoing this evening.'

As I was drying myself, old Di came up again. There was not much point in getting yourself dry; the act of towelling was enough to bring you out in a muck sweat.

'How about it, Horry, lad? You got to break out now and again.'

'What was all that you were telling me about keeping away from Indian women?'

'You got to break out now and again, bach, haven't you, now? My mate and I'll take you along and show you the ropes.'

'Oh, you and Taff go on your own. I've got to do my blancoing or I'll be on a thick'un again.'

'It isn't Taff. It's a mucker of mine down in M/T. Jock McGuffie. He's a real cure.'

Nobody had ever accused Di of being a whoremonger; and there was his manner; he looked too quiet and pious, though he made a good forward. There was also his dick; in an obscure way, I felt it would be demeaning to go out fucking with a chap with a dick like his. Yet there was something in his confident unobtrusive manner, you had to admire: the sort of bod you were proud to associate with, even in a whorehouse.

As I climbed into my trousers, I said, 'The bloody bazaar's swarming with Redcaps, Di. I'll tell you that for nothing.'

'Oh, we shan't be daft enough to go there! My mucker's got other ideas. We'll go off in his truck.'

That made it sound more exciting. Besides, who knew when there would be another chance?

'You know me, mate – I'm shit or bust! What about Taffy?

'He's not coming. He's afraid his old woman'd find out.'

'What about your old woman, Di?'

'She'll never find out!' He winked. 'She's too far away.'

When I had dressed, I marched back to the barrack-room and took my kit down to the yard, to begin blanco operations instead of hitting my *charpoy*. Di and I agreed to meet down at the M/T office at seven-thirty.

As I was lugging my harness downstairs, I met old Bamber coming up. He was clutching a wad of mail.

'There's a couple of letters for you, Horry – something to read while you're down there bullshitting. I suppose you wouldn't do my big pack for me while you're in the mood?'

'Get stuffed!'

I opened my mail downstairs, after dumping the equipment on a trestle table. Both letters were from my mother.

Mother wrote amusing letters. She was good at quoting things people said, or telling me stories about neighbours I hardly remembered. She had joined the WVS since I left home, and generally had something funny to tell me which had occurred to her in her canteen. When all else failed, she would fall back on a joke she had heard on a wireless programme, *Workers' Playtime,* or *Mapleleaf Matinee,* or *The Jack Benny Show.* She told me that Ann had been to a party at the Cleavers' (whoever they were). She had heard from Nelson in Italy, who had a streaming cold. About herself she only said that she was taking regular afternoon walks; yesterday, she had gone as far as the gravel-pits (I couldn't visualize them).

It all left a curious desolation in my breast. For I never wrote to her. I had sent an airgraph when we first arrived at Kanchapur, so that the family would know our convoy had not been sunk on its way to India; since then, I had not been able to write a line.

At the time, I could not decide whether this was to be reckoned a sad failure or a sure sign of an evil nature. I began by being genuinely unable to convey my impressions about India, and the Army tradition encouraged my weaknesses, for youngsters who never wrote home were regarded as 'dogs', whereas lads like Jackie Tertis, who were forever writing home, were regarded as soft.

So every letter from my mother made me feel bad. Sometimes she reproached me, and then I was full of grief and resentment; but when she wrote – as now – without a word of reproach, the effect was worse, for I had to suffer self-reproach.

'Oh Christ, I musn't be such a bad bastard,' I told myself as I bent over the blanco, in a sudden reversion to childhood patterns of thought induced by the letters I had rammed guiltily into my pocket. 'Whatever would Mum think of me? I mustn't go out on the bash tonight, I really mustn't. . . .'

The dreaded Rusk slouched by, with his mate Locke, a villainous fellow with broken brown teeth, heading for the cookhouse.

'Going to dish up some more soyer-links, Rusk?' I called.

'Bull-shitting again, Stubbs? After getting them stripes back again, then? You want to get some service in first, don't he, George?'

'I suppose you'll be down the cinema getting a basinful of Betty Grable tonight, Stubby?' Locke called. They were still dragging towards the cookhouse, not looking back as they spoke.

'You know what you can do with Betty Grable, Locke!'

'After you with Betty Grable!'

'You lads can have her. I'm off out on the nest myself, this evening.'

That did make Rusk look back. 'Dirty bastard!' he called approvingly.

Why did I, I asked myself, why did I have to try and impress horrible shits like the cooks? There was a weak and wicked streak in my nature. Supposing I caught a dose of the pox this evening? That meant the old Umbrella Treatment, terrifying accounts of which circulated in the Mendips. And they stamped the word 'Syphilis' on your discharge papers, so that all future employers were warned about you, or so Aylmer claimed. Still, I had a long while left to serve – I could not expect to hang on to my virginity for seven-and-five, could I?

And it was not just a good shag I needed. It was romance. It was, as I once heard an old soldier poetically express it, getting to know the heart of a country through the eye in your knob. 'The unknown She' – that was what I wanted;

[114]

an insight into the whole strange alluring-repugnant charge
of India.

That face came back to me, staring at me through iron
bars. The burning body, the twot like sucked marzipan, the
dark melting eyes, the straight nose, the small mouth, the
⸱ ⸱ ssion – of what? Of longing? Somewhere there must be
a woman whose longings corresponded to mine. Perhaps she
could be found, that unknown She, even within the confines
of a knocking shop.

With similar hopeful thoughts, accompanied by a slight
stirring in the trousers in the region of my field-dressing
pocket, I trooped down to the M/T section at 1930 hours.

Di Jones was already there. The area was deserted, the
offices and garages all closed, the five-tonners standing in an
immaculate line, spaced equidistant apart on the concrete –
except for one lorry, which had its engine running. A small
sandy-haired Scot, whom I knew as Jock McGuffie, was
angrily polishing up its headlights with a cloth and carrying
on a monologue which my arrival did not deflect in any way.

'Well, I see you're all togged up, Stubby-lad!', exclaimed
Di, patting me jovially on the shoulder. 'It's really snazzy
you look!'

'– so anyhow, I said to him, "Look, Corporal Fucking
Warren," I said, "when I'm off duty, I'm off duty, whether
you may happen to like it or not, and what I do when I'm
off duty happens to be my own fucking business", I told
him. He looked at me as if he was fair fit to explode! "See
these fucking tapes", he says, pointing to his stripes, "What
do you think they are, birdshit?", he says. "Any more lip
from you," he says, "and I'll have you up at the company
duftah so bloody fast your feet won't touch," he says. Aye, he
was fair flaming mad! So I says to him, "Oh, we'll see about
that," I says. "It's no good you pulling your rank at me," I
says. "I've been on the mat more times than you've had
NAAFI suppers, and if you think I'm whitewashing fucking

stones at four-thirty in the afternoon for you," I says, "then you've got another think coming!' I told him.'

While this monologue and more was in progress, and the lights of the vehicle were gleaming ever more brightly, I was standing about with some embarrassment. Di was listening in a relaxed way. I grew impatient, wishing he would introduce me to McGuffie, to whom I had never spoken; but in the ranks all are reckoned to be buddies, and there are no introductions. The annoying thing was that this buddy seemed not to have noticed me.

Eventually, Jock interrupted his own monologue, with a grudging 'Och, we'd better be on the move if we're going to move!', and we climbed up into the cab with him.

It appeared that he had had an extensive argument with the unlucky Corporal Fucking Warren, triumphing in point after conversational point. Between his verbatim reports on this, he informed us that we were going to Indore, officially to deliver something he called Furniture, office, desk one, clerks for the use of.

'We'll have a bit of a booze, Di, and then drop in on this knocking shop, okay? So this other bloke comes up and just stands there sort of looking like, so I puts my brush down and I says to him, "And what are you fucking staring at, mate?", I asks. "Have you no' seen a man on fucking jankers before?" So he gets all nasty then. "I've done more jankers than you've seen pay-parades," he says. "Then you can do my fucking jankers for me," I tells him, "if you're so fucking keen!". . .'

I rolled the window down and we moved through the barrier at the gate, where McGuffie had shown his pass without breaking the flow of his discourse. All about us was India, as ever tangible as a warm breath on the cheek, its electric forces such that the voluptuous evening sky flickered constantly. What a mystery! And somewhere ahead, in some filthy dodgey little building was a young girl – sold into prostitution by her impoverished parents – who would recognize me and come lovingly into my arms. If the eloquent McGuffie did this run regularly, I could visit her regularly. How much could I afford a week out of my beggarly pay?

Di nudged me. 'Wake up, Stubby! Jock's asking you if you're much of a boozer?'

'I'm looking forward to getting at the *bibis*,' I told him.

'Are you now? Well, we're going to have a wee drink first, if it's all the same to you, seeing as this is my excursion!'

'Good.' I had to make myself agreeable. 'I could do with a beer.'

'Could you now? You'll no' be buying the first round, I suppose?'

'*Thik-hai*. I don't mind buying the first round.'

'Och, well, you may have t' buy all the fucking rounds, laddie, for I haven' an anna till pay-day!' Struck by the humour of this, McGuffie roared with laughter and we nearly ran down a couple of Wogs by the roadside. Fortunately, they were young and agile. Di also was laughing, which seemed unnecessary.

'How are you going to pay for your *bibi*, then?' I asked.

'Oh, they'll let old Jock McGuffie in for free – he's only got a wee one!' He and Di Jones bellowed with laughter again. This time I joined in too; any man who could make jokes about the smallness of his tool was obviously a real humourist.

'Indeed, the terrible fellow has a weapon on him like a cucumber,' Di said, still laughing.

'How much do you reckon they'll charge, Di?' I asked. 'Will it be more than five chips?'

'Will you stop worrying, sonny? Och, with the three of us going in together, they'll let us have it wholesale!' More laughter.

Through the window, the lights of Indore shone ahead:

dull, sullen, guttering lights, just as I had hoped. We bumped through the ghastly outskirts, where a small market was being held. Figures were everywhere, adults interwoven with fast-moving lads; faces with bright eyes, lit by solitary oil-lamps, to be distinguished behind counters or piles of fruit. As always, there was music and stink – the basic senses were never segregated in United Provinces. I hung out of the window, intoxicated by it all. There were cows ambling about the paths or jostling between stalls, ancestral motor-cars trundling beside us, and men in topees, though starlight was upon us. We passed an enormous factory – 'Cotton,' Di Jones said, wisely – and I glimpsed dozens of men parading under a corrugated-iron roof, picked out by floodlights. Then we were moving between blocks of flats, and could see how they teemed with life on every storey. What sort of incredible life could go on in there?! As if asking themselves the same question, huge pink faces of film stars glared down at us from above a cinema, their features picked out in green and mauve. With a shock, I recognized they were intended to be Alan Ladd and Veronica Lake, viewed through the distorting waters of Hindu culture.

It was impossible to decide where the centre of an Indian town was. There was no centre. We stopped at a non-centre and were instantly surrounded by beggars. Jock McGuffie jumped to the ground.

'Fuck off out of here, you ragged-arsed heathens! Get fucking weaving the lot o' ye, before I get a machine-gun to you and do for you once for all!'

We climbed down, and I asked (Oh God, we were nearly there!) nervously, 'Are you going to deliver the office desk, Jock?'

'Deliver the office desk? Eh, Di, you've got a right one here and no mistake! Deliver the office desk, is it? Look, sonny, I'm no' delivering any fucking desk for you nor anybody in my free time, I'm telling you! I stop work at

four, sharp, I do, war or no war, sonny boy, and that's
your lot –'

'Okay, okay, I just thought that's why we came to
Indore –'

'Did you, now? Well, it wasna what *I* came to Indore for,
I can tell you that for free, eh, Di?'

'I came for a beer,' Di said, adding, 'Stubby's a good old
boy-o, it's just he didn't grasp like that the desk was what you
might call an official pretext.'

'That bloody desk stays in my *gharri* until I say otherwise,'
Jock said savagely. He grabbed one of the Indians standing
about and told him to guard the lorry until we returned. The
chap was very dark and shining, with yellow eyes, and sores
all down one leg. He smiled tolerantly.

'How much you give me, sahib?'

'We'll give you five rupees between us, Johnny, *thik-hai*?
Five rupees, *paunch rupee*. *Malum*? You guard it proper,
Johnny. What's your name?'

'Ali, sahib.'

'Och, you're all called fucking Ali! No' a fucking Donald
among you! Can't you think of any other bastarding name
to call yourselves but Ali? What's your other name? *Tumhara
nahm kia hai*?'

'*Baraf*, sahib.' The man giggled, and the crowd giggled in
sympathy. Jock silenced them with a look.

'Not a fucking MacPherson among the bloody lot!
Thik-hai, Ali Bugger-Off, you guard my *gharri* till I get back,
malum? And if anybody so much as lays a finger on it, I'll
have your guts for garters, okay?'

We walked off, leaving Ali Baraf in charge.

Di looked thoughtful. 'Five chips is a lot of moolah, Jock,
man.'

Jock stared at him incredulously. 'A lot of moolah, is it?
You don't think we're going to pay the puir wee bastard,
do you, 'cos if so you've got another think coming!'

'You should keep your word to the lower races or they will never respect you.'

Jock threw back his head and laughed. 'You fucking ignorant Welsh git, you! Don't tell me that puir wee bastard expects to get paid! – He's guarding that truck for the privilege of it, nothing more. He knows as well as I do that if he makes a fuss when we get back, I'll kick his arse right out of his fucking dhoti!'

The state of Indore was one of the Princely States; in some of the more independent ones, like Hyderabad, the Army was almost entirely banned; here, it was allowed only on sufferance, and we saw few troops. Bold as brass, we marched up the middle of the crowded street, calling and laughing – much like the people round us, only they were less pugnacious about it.

Trees grew on either side of the road. Goats were tied to many of them, nibbling at the bark so vigorously that it was a wonder the trees survived. Trams clattered by, packed with people, decked with people, sending their blue sparks among the leaves of the trees. Insects bumped about the hanging street-lights, to splash at our feet. Beggars with heroic deformities lay juddering in the gutter, men peed against walls, hawkers shouted their wares. The universe was crammed with life, bursting from the foetid loins of Brahma.

'Dirty buggers! It's worse than Sauchihall Street on a fine Saturday – ye canna hear yourself speak!'

'Cardiff was never like this!'

A man ran up and tried to sell us a carpet. Jock dismissed him and turned down a side street. It was darker here, and more barbarous. A hotel stood on one side, a balcony above its main door.

'We'll sit up there!' Jock said, pointing.

'Looks pretty full,' I said. The balcony was crowded with black faces.

'They'll make room for us. I know the proprietor.

I've been here before. Just you let old Jock take care of
you.'

So we barged in, into a crowded and shabby little dining-
room. Jock started roaring for service and the manager came
up. He was huge and ungainly and wore a light blue
Western-style suit. His crumpled brown face lit with delight
at the sight of Jock.

'So, you escape from the detention again, Mr Jock!'

'Och, then, you're still here, you fucking robber! They
haven't cut your throat yet! Have you chucked out that
dirty manky beer you poisoned me with last time I came?'

'We keep some special beer to finish you up this time.'

'Getting your own back on the British Raj, eh?'

'Yes, yes, ha ha, I get my own back on the British Raj! I
kill all men with the filthy Indian beer!'

'Kill the officers first, that's all I ask.'

'We kill the officers first and the Scotchmen last.'

Jock roared with laughter, and he and the proprietor
clumped upstairs, patting each other on the back – quite a
feat, since Jock was almost a yard smaller than the Indian.
Di and I followed.

'Get a few beers inside us, Stubby,' Di said. 'Then we'll
tackle these *bibis*. Don't be impatient. Get yourself fortified
properly.'

'I need a woman.'

Jock heard my remark. To his Indian friend he said,
'Our young Sassenach pal here, he's fair desperate to get the
dirty water off his chest! Are you selling your daughter
again tonight?'

'Yes, yes, I sell my daughter. Very much recommend.'

'You tried her out last night yourself, eh, you old sod, you!
Bring us some beer first – and this time, don't fucking piss in
it in the kitchen, eh?'

'No, no, tonight I not piss in the beer! Next time you come
I do it.'

'You try it and you'll get a bunch of fives right in your clock!'

Laughing, he showed us on to the balcony – crowded, as I had observed from the street, mainly with portly Indians eating snacks or drinking local hooch. The proprietor went over to one table and, with a multitude of gesture, persuaded the four men sitting at it to leave. They rose reluctantly, frowning in our direction.

'Don't you pull you bloody faces at me!' Jock exclaimed. 'Come on, speed it up, *jao*, we haven't got our own back for the Black Hole of Calcutta yet, and don't you pack of *babus* forget it!'

'Seems a bit hard when they're enjoying their evening,' Di said.

'A bit hard? Are you out your fucking mind, Di? These bastards sit here getting fat drinking their bastard *todi*, and if it wasna for the British they be kissing some fat Japanese arse by now, wouldn't they? They should be fucking grateful. Away with you, you miserable foreign gits!'

We sat down. A waiter rushed to bring bottles of beer, sloshing the liquid quickly into three glasses.

'Ahh! Gnat's piss!' exclaimed Jock, drinking deep. 'More beer, you slack bastards! Keep it coming! Dinne stop till you see it spurt from my ears!'

An hour later, we were still there drinking. It was pleasant on the balcony. The mosquitoes were not biting too much and the beer – despite my haunting suspicion that the proprietor had surely pissed in it – was tolerable. Jock had quietened down now that all his wants were being attended to and was telling us some unlikely stories; Di and I had to do no more than supply a sort of chorus.

The next time Jock called for another round, I said, 'No more for me, Jock. There are other things I want to be doing.'

'No more beer? You canne be full already, sonny! Have

another drink like a man! Waiter, *ither ao*, three more beers, *jhaldi* – and for Jesus' sake make it three that haven't been standing in the sun all fucking day. You're like all the fucking English, Stubby, you canne take your liquor! Why, you're no' even *smoking* seriously!'

'Oh no? Then where the fucking hell do you think most of this twenty packet of Wog Players has gone? Up my arse?'

'You don't call that *smoking*, do you? You're just an amateur at it, isn't he, Di? I tell you, I was smoking before I was weaned. Aye, I was! Smoking before I was weaned! My ma couldna afford to feed me, so she kept me at the tittie until I was three years old, by which time I was filching Woodies off my older brothers. Now get this beer down your throat and don't piss about.'

'I don't want any more beer, fuck it, I want some fucking intercourse – get that through your sodding thick Glaswegian head!'

'This is the sort of tricky bastard we were up agin at Bannockburn!'

'Let's go over to the whorehouse, Jock – we can have another drink afterwards,' Di said.

'Are you two ganging up on me? I havene started drinking!' But he poured the beer a little faster down his throat and finally scraped his chair back. I rose in relief and found that the weak beer had a certain effect.

The proprietor came hurrying, flexing every crease in his blue suit. The business of paying went more smoothly than I had expected. It appeared that Jock had some money, after all. As he settled up, the manager called a boy to run round to the brothel and announce our coming.

'Come on round with us, man – nobody will pocket the silver!'

'No, no, I must decline. You go and enjoy the girls.'

'The girls? No' a one under fifty! I'll watch it I don't get stuck into your daughter or the teeth will be rotting out of my head in a week!' With such pleasantries, we staggered down the stairs and into the street.

'You friend very funny man!' the proprietor said, flashing a golden smile on Di and me. He ducked back into the hotel and closed the door.

We were surrounded by touts and ponces, all calling to us. The urchin despatched to the brothel had undoubtedly called our business loudly down the street, and now every pimp in town was out to waylay us.

'Dear Lord, but it's a terrible depraved country!' Di exclaimed, making a lot of his clicking noises, as bargain bunk-ups were pressed on us from all sides. 'If my poor missus could see me now, she'd throw herself down the nearest well!'

'If mine were here, we could all have a free bash!' Jock roared, striking out at the nearest ponces.

The brothel was only a few houses down from the hotel. Full of excitement and anxiety, I followed the other two in through its battered double doors. A mournful old man sitting in a dim vestibule pointed upstairs. Up we went, Jock first, then Di, then I, our boots clumping on the bare stairway. With my face almost in Di's arse, I nevertheless saw visions of lustrous naked maidens.

Dim lighting revealed a landing with a corridor off it. The landing had been converted into a sort of two-woman laundry. Cramped into small space, two old crones sat on the floor repairing sheets. Most of the illumination came from a street-light hanging outside the window. Another old crone appeared and nodded at us.

'Hello there, gran! What do you do? Gobble? Where are the birds? We want three as are fit enough to stand a gude shafting.'

We became involved in a haggle. The rules of the house seemed to dictate that we did not even see the girls until we had paid something. Then it would be ten rupees each, short time. Jock argued fiercely against this arrangement; I grew impatient with him, and would have paid; but eventually he won the day, and we pushed forward to the corridor. Jock flung open the first door.

I pressed for a look in over his shoulder.

'Christ, you randy bugger! Don't crowd me! This is my choice – try your luck in one of the other doors!'

As I passed on, he cried, 'Come out, you bag, and let Jock have a *shufti* at you!'

As my eyes grew used to the gloom, I saw that the other doors were all open, or at least ajar. Eyes were watching us. At the end of the corridor, a man was lurking. Of course, he could have been another customer. A fear of being knifed rose in me. I remembered – now of all times – that there had been riots in Indore only the month before.

Still, here we were. My visions had yielded to a sordid and ill-smelling reality, but here we were, and Di was pushing into another door, so I also went forward.

It was extremely dark. The first thing I made out was that all the corridor doors opened into the same long room, which was divided by curtains. Standing up, I could see over the top of the curtains. The only lighting came from outside, a yellow light sliding obliquely through filthy panes. Ahead of me was a bed covered by dark bedding. Joss sticks were burning, filling the air with drowsy smoke. A girl stood by the door, and thus almost against me.

'Hello, sweetheart!' she said.

'Hello! What's your name?'

'Hello, sweetheart. You like jig-jig?'

'That's the idea. Let's look at you first.' I took hold of her shoulder and tried to lead her over to the ray of light. She said something – she spoke almost no English. All we had in common was the word, the call-sign, "jig-jig". Di and Jock were going through the same routine close by on either side of me.

I heard Jock's voice roaring away. 'Och, girl, let's have a fucking dekko at your clock. Stand bloody still, will you? I'm no' going to hurt you, not unless you keep wriggling about.' He struck a match. Good idea, I thought.

When I struck a match, I saw that one of the old crones from the landing had followed me in and now stood close behind me, waiting. I took in the filth on the ceiling, the tears in the partition-curtaining, and then I turned to my beauty. She put her hand up to her face. The match, being an Indian one, failed and went out.

Jock was still audible. 'Away with you, you old bag of bones, I'm no going to grind my pizzle to a point in ye! Away and fetch your grand-daughter! . . . Oh, that's better . . . ah . . . yon's no' a bad body ye have there, considering it's been around since Mafekin . . .'

'How're you doing, Jock?' I called, striking another match.

'You've led me into temptation, sonny! She's an ugly old nelly, but she loves me. Besides, you don't look at the mantle-piece while you're poking the fire . . .'

My *bibi* pushed my matches away and began to cling to me. The old crone behind me was muttering advice or encouragement. The girl started to feel my balls, trying at the same time to get me down on the bed. I imagined it swarming with bedbugs and resisted, angry but at the same time increasingly excited. She had my flies open and was now tugging at my tool in a fairly urgent way. This had no effect, since I could feel how gnarled her hand was. I was convinced she was a century old. Disgust and lust struggled in me. Lust was winning by a short head, my tool was stirring in blind response to treatment, when the old crone by the door misjudged her moment and came forward to sell me a french letter for two rupees.

'Fuck off, you ancient whore!' I roared and she retreated without argument. I stood there unresisting, letting the *bibi* try to rouse my reluctant member, and listening to what Di was doing.

It sounded to me as if he was already on the job, having his bunk-up, as he called it. He was making clicking noises with his tongue, as if disapproving of his own activities. What a man! It was hard to visualize that inch of candle – now no doubt stretched to three inches – working away in some greasy groove; equally, it was difficult to imagine the quiet god-fearing Di Jones in a posture so different from the one he assumed in Bethesda every Sunday at home. Sex was the most amazing activity!

Unlikely though it seemed, I now had a hard-on: seven-and-a-half inches of broad-minded gristle. I sat on the fearful bed. The woman started to fawn over me. There was no question of being able to establish any sort of communication with her. We should never discover twin souls in each other's eyes. Stiff as my prick was, the rest of my flesh crawled with disgust at her touch.

I was still resolved to see her. I struck another match and grabbed her wrist before she could put her hand to her face – in a gesture of shame?

'Look at me, you bitch!' She turned her head away. I twisted her wrist. With a silent cry, she looked cringingly at me, over the flame of the match.

She was not young. Nor was she ancient. She was not pretty. Her face was puffy and shapeless, appearing yellow in the light of the flame. Her hair was done into pigtails. Her teeth looked good. On her upper lip were the first lashes of a putative moustache. She stared at me with an unfathomable expression, and then the match went out.

What had I been expecting a moment before? Horror or beauty? Only half-aware of what was happening, I let her press me back on to the bed: it was the best way to avoid being kissed by her, something I very much wanted to avoid. The sounds of Di, the roar of Jock, came to me, as I submitted to this treatment. The crone was standing closer, sod her guts, still bloody muttering instructions.

My *bibi* – my *bibi*, already worn and degraded by hundreds of foul drink- and pox-riddled sods! – swarmed over me, reaching up to stroke my hair and undo my shirt buttons, to stroke my chest and feel into my armpit.

'There's no fucking money up there,' I told her. 'Get on with it, damn you!'

My cock was in no state of indecision. It gave a throb as it felt her breath, her poisonous breath, on it. Its knob swelled, and it was engulfed by her lips, raked deliciously along the rough palate of her mouth and brought to rest luxuriously against her epiglottis. Her teeth and her tongue teased it. You had to say that for the bloody woman: she was practised at her trade. I sprawled there, staring down at her dark anonymous head as she worked the trick.

A little later, we were staggering back down the street, singing loudly, and laughing to think of the bollicking we were going to give Ali Bugger-Off when we got back to Jock's truck.

We did an hour's square-bashing after parade next morning. My years at public school had taught me quick responses and slavish obedience, if nothing else, so that I usually avoided trouble. This morning, I was in trouble all the time, constantly being bawled out by Sergeant Meadows.

On the one hand, I was vexed and disappointed that the contact with the *bibi* had been so commercial, so perfunctory – why, I had not even seen or touched her snatch; on the other hand, I had been gobbled for the first time in my life, an undoubted step towards maturity. On the one hand, that gobble had been so debasing: the hunching of her body over my belly had expressed degradation in every line, and so I also had been degraded; on the other hand, wow, the sheer sensation of it as her tongue had teased the last jolt of power from my nerves – hadn't I been so abandoned that I had buried my face in the stinking blanket?

It had all been so killingly mercenary! I was still groaning when the old hag was demanding *paisa* from me. Jock had a haggle over money, claiming he was being charged too much. And as I emerged on to the landing, four drunken British squaddies – not from the Mendips – were getting ready to take our places, as if it was a fish-and-chip queue.

What could have been more squalid? And yet part of me was thrilled, privileged, to be part of such degradation. For wasn't this what went on over most of the globe – not in England, maybe, but almost everywhere else? As Di Jones put it, 'You couldn't explain to anyone at home what conditions is like out here.'

Squalid as it had been, it had been something else besides. A vile disappointment, yes – yet I was moved by the memory of that plain face lit by match-flame, so close to me, so defenceless! It plagued me that I could never know anything more about her, how she lived, how she suffered, where she had been born, how she had come to this dreary pass, shut in a stuffy room, sucking as many stinking yards of cock as came her way.

No wonder I was never in step on the parade ground that morning! I was thinking of my father, looking up at me as I jumped on to the bus platform. 'Be a good boy and don't go into any brothels' – had he really said that? And his face receding, anxious, ever anxious, as the bus rolled away down the road. Or perhaps he had said, 'Don't go emptying too many bottles.'

After parade, and one last bollicking from Charley Meadows, we were detailed for fatigues. I went over to where No. 1 Platoon, its heels up against a wall, was fallen out for a smoke, and looked out Di.

As we hung about, smoking an inch of fag, he asked me quietly, 'How you doing this morning?'

'Great! I've got a bit of a hangover and my knob's sore, otherwise I'm smashing.'

'Be serious, Horry! You're not sorry I took you along last night?'

So his Welsh conscience was playing him up!

'Di, just between you and me, how was your *bibi*?'

'How was yours?'

'Oh, okay.'

'Not a raddled old hag?'

'No – no, nothing like that. Proper little beauty, really. It was hard to be sure, but I'd say she was about eighteen or nineteen. I didn't half give her a bashing! She loved it!' I groaned to convey what rapture I had experienced. 'I'd have had another go if I'd got the cash. You got on okay, did you?'

He looked cautious. 'You got a better deal than what I did. Just my bloody luck to go through the wrong door. . .' He hesitated. 'She was a bit of a raddled old hag, you'd have to say it . . . I was afraid of getting a dose off her. So I just – well, I sat on the edge of the bed like and just let her toss me off. It seemed safest. Don't tell old Jock, will you? He'd only laugh! And she'd got hands like sandpaper, honest she had.'

Feeling shamed by his honesty, I clapped him on the back. 'Better luck next time, Di!'

'They ought to have proper government brothels, that's what, same as the Italian army.'

'Do the Italians have government whore-houses then?'

'Pukka clean places, inspected every week. Nice girls too, so I hear. Jack Aylmer was saying as Italian officers and men all go to the same brothel. Of course, they're Roman Catholic. . . .'

This fascinating conversation was brought to an end by Corporals Warren and Dutt descending on us. Di went off on rations and I was given the job of refilling the buckets at the various fire-points round the camp.

While I was on this absorbing task, and taking as long as possible over it, I heard a piercing whistle. Jock McGuffie was leaning out of a cookhouse window. I waved and indicated that I had a job to do. After a while, I saw that he was coming over towards me, his face more colourless than ever in the bright sunlight. Jock began talking while he was still several yards from me.

'What, are you after promotion or something, Stubbs, bullshitting away here in the heat? You must be kind of eager or why didn't you come on over to the cookhouse when I gave you the sign? I was scrounging a mug of *char* off the fucking cooks, seeing as how them whores robbed me of my last anna last night – not that it's what you might call anything better than dishwater, that stuff they dole out –'

'What do you expect with that sod Rusk fucking about in there?'

'Och, old Rusty's no' sae bad, considering he comes from Carlisle, of all mankey fuckin' places. At least he'll slip you an egg-butty now and again, which is more than you can say for yon big fat sergeant-cook. I had a mate from Paisley as had slippped his wife a length or two in his time, and he reckoned she was as fat and greasy as what Nobby is.'

Two minutes later, we were relaxing in the canteen over two glasses of beer, while Jock told me about a long-past feud between Sergeants Gowland and Meadows in which he had been involved.

'So bloody Gowland says, "You know you can get a long stretch in the glasshouse for falling asleep on guard duty?", he says, so I says to him, "I was resting my eyes, sar'nt," I says, "and your torch dazzled me. You ask my mate Morris and he'll tell you." So he bellows for my mate Morris –'

'They never put one over on you, Jock, do they?'

He stopped in mid-spate and eyed me suspiciously. 'Do you

want to borrow some cash, is it? I told you, you're paying
for this beer and I'll owe it to you. They're always putting it
over on me – it's fucking victimization, that's what it is! If
your face doesn't fit, you're in the shit all the time, and
you've got to fight back as best you can.'

'Last night was okay, wasn't it?'

'Same as any other fucking night!' He was still suspicious,
and pinched one of my fags and lit it up. It was cool and quiet
in the canteen, with a buzzing fly to emphasize the silence.
The sound of a squad being drilled came distantly to us.

'What was that *bibi* like you had?'

'What like was she? How d'you mean, What like was she?
She was good enough for a blow-through. One woman's
just the same as the fucking next as far as I'm concerned.'

He was always reticent about sex. Removing his fag from
his mouth with a quick gesture, he changed the subject.

'Look, Stubby, lad, you know that this fucking brigade
won't be in the land of the blow-through much longer.'

'How's that?'

'Christ-on-fucking-crutches! You're a bit dim this morning, aren't you? You bloody English, you live so soft your
wits congeal in your thick heads! We'll be moving into
action soon – straight into the fucking jungle, tangling it
with the Japs!'

'Sure, we came out here to fight a war, didn't we?'

He dragged despairingly on his cigarette. 'You may have
done, mate – I fucking didn't!'

I gave him a laugh. 'Come on, Jock, serving King and
Country and all that!'

'Och, what's the fucking king ever done for me? I'm no'
planning to stick my fucking neck out for him, I'll tell you
that for free.'

'You know the rumours – since the Arakan's out, 2 Div
will probably be going to Assam. We've got no option.'

'Ah, balls! It's a case of exercising the prerogatives. Listen

to me!' He leaned forward, fixing his little sharp gaze on me.
'I'm telling you, within a week of now, this fucking shower is
going to be moving east at a rate of knots, right? All except
some. And who will that some be?'

'Baggage party?'

'Too fucking true! Rear baggage party. If you play your
cards right, you can get on to rear baggage party.'

I looked doubtful. 'I suppose you could get on the sick
list and be in hospital when the unit moved out.'

'Hospital? *Hospital*? Are you out of your fucking head?
They'll bounce you straight into Field Ambulance. I know
some of those bloody M.O.s in Field Ambulance – they
aren't fit to be in charge of pigs. They'd bounce you right
into the front line if you were dying of dysentery! No, you got
to work a flanker. Och, I'll no' pretend it's easy, but there are
ways. And the first thing to do is to pick your officer.'

Jock lived on a different wavelength from me. He grabbed
my arm. 'You think I'm pulling your pisser, man? Listen,
pick your officer! They're fucking human, same as you, you
know!'

This was rank heresy in the Army. I had it drummed into
me continuously that officers were a different species, and
had never had grounds for doubting it.

'I tell you they're fucking human, no matter what like the
cunts may act when we're around. Some of them wants to go
to death and glory, some of them are shitting themselves at
the thought of a shot fired in anger – same as anyone. You're
under Spunk Bucket, aren't you?'

'Who?'

'Gor-Blimey. Captain Eric Gore-Blakeley. He's one of the
buggers who doesn't mind if he boozes his whole life away
miles behind the lines.' All the time we were sitting in the
canteen, Jock's little ferretty eyes were rarely on me, always
elsewhere – particularly on the doorway.

'How do you know all this, Jock?'

'Och, I'm a student of fucking psychology! You have to keep your eyes and ears open in this world or you get a knife in the ribs.'

'What were you in Civvy Street, Jock?'

He did look at me then, for a moment. 'What that got to do with it? No, I've driven that Gor-Blimey of yours all round the place in my time. Him and me understand each other – I know him as well as I know the crabs on my own balls! They officers manoeuvre for position, same as the rest of us. Spunk Bucket's no more keen to soldier in Burma that what I am. In my form book, he's the likeliest officer in "A" Company to wangle a number on rear baggage party. So he'll pick the men he wants. So, he will want men he can trust, ginks who feel the same as he does. So, you'd better get yourself picked for rear detail, and fast!'

'And you?'

'I can look after myself.'

'How do I get myself picked?'

'Christ, and you a fucking Signaller! Let him see you're a dodgey bastard too! I'm off now – through the bar, must have a pee! See you!'

He disappeared with surprising rapidity, dodging behind the bar and out the back before the Indian orderly could protest. I looked around. We had been the only two in the canteen at this relatively early hour. Now boots were approaching, marching smartly. Jock had heard them before I did. I was caught; Jock had vanished.

The door opened, there was a cry of 'Honey Pears', and Enoch Ford and Wally Page marched in, swinging their arms smartly right up to my table, some other squaddies pressing in behind them.

'Company, Company, halt! Company – wait for it! – Company, dis – MISS!'

As they fell themselves out, I told them they were in time to buy me another drink.

'Drinking on your fucking own now, Stubbs!' said Wally. 'You're after them bastard stripes back, don't tell me!'

'I was having a drink with Jock McGuffie.'

'Strewth, don't let *him* give you two sixpences for a shilling or you'll end up elevenpence short, I'm telling you. He wouldn't even tell you the correct time, Jock McGuffie.'

Enoch came over with the beers, slopping them as he came. Wally told him, 'Young Stubby has been drinking with Jock McGuffie.'

'He's a right one, he is! He wouldn't give you the time of day, wouldn't Jock. He never lifted owt off anyone, and that's as true as I'm standing here riding this bicycle. Wally'll tell you same.'

'I never believe a word either of you buggers tell me. He's all right, is McGuffie – knows how to look after himself.'

Wally settled comfortably down with his elbows on the table. 'Get some service in, fucking Stubbs! That little Scots bugger is all for Number One okay! He would have the fucking shirt off your fucking back. You've been keeping some funny company lately – it's all them pox-ridden Wog gods, that's what it is. Where were you last night when we were waiting to go down to the WVS?'

'He was out with the taffies,' Enoch said. 'You missed a bloody good evening, Stubby, you did! You missed bloody Betty Grable in her bath. I wouldn't mind slipping her a length, I tell you!' He made wanking movements up to his chest, banging the back of his neck at the same time. 'Wherrr! Git in there, Nobby!'

'I can see Betty Grable any time. That goes for her fucking bath, too – we've got fucking baths at home.'

'Then you're bloody lucky, mate, that's all I can say.' Enoch's big beaming flat face never lost its smile. 'Back in our house, we all have to take a turn under the kitchen tap, same as the neighbours. By Christ, that sort of thing is going to change after the war, let me tell you! The

Communist Party's going to do something for those who've fought, or the blood'll run in the fucking streets!'

'All right, we all know you come from up North,' Wally said. 'Things ain't much better round our way. We all washed in the kitchen same as you, and there was only one proper bed between the seven of us.'

'Then it's about time you stopped voting for Churchill and that mob, i'n't it?' Enoch said.

'Churchill's okay – he knows the worth of the working man.'

'Up your flue! He was only shooting at them in the General Strike, that's all!'

'Old Blighty would have been defeated by the Krauts by now, but for Churchill, and don't you forget it!'

In these discussions, I was always put out of countenance, feeling I had not suffered enough. As I handed the cigarettes round, I cringed in case Enoch accused me of a capitalist gesture; but Enoch was a kind-hearted lad, and had no thought of embarrassing me. He accepted my cigarette.

When he remarked that I had still not revealed where I had been the previous evening, I told them I got a lift into Indore. Wally pounced at once.

'Get knotted, Stubbs! Indore's out of fucking bounds, for crying out loud. You know that! Officers only. No dogs or BORs.'

'I tell you I was in fucking Indore. You want to wash your ears out.'

'Fuck off, mate! You never been to Indore in your natural!'

'I suppose that was sodding Blackpool I was in last night?'

'Honey Pears!' cried Enoch. 'I wish Blackpool was that near. I'd catch the first bloody train back to Werriton, I can tell you. You wouldn't see me for dust!'

'What was you doing in Indore, anyhow? Shagging your arse off, I bet!'

'We just went over for a drink in Jock's *gharri*.'

[136]

'Drinking with the drivers, eh, Stubbs? You boozy bastard, your own fucking mates ain't good enough for you. That's it, eh? What was the beer like?'

'Good stuff.'

'Piss off! "Good beer", he says! You can't get good beer in India. Not like the jammy buggers liberating Italy, guzzling down all that Kraut beer!'

'And fucking well fucking the I-tie girls!' said Enoch. This was a safer subject. I joined in a chorus that we had already learnt by heart after only a few weeks in India.

'They get fags flown out from England, and Yank rations and Yank beer. No wonder they are stuck where they are – they're too pissed to fight!'

'And if you get wounded in Italy, they fly you back to Blighty – not like bloody Burma. You can die in Burma and do you think anyone at home cares? Not on your fucking nelly!'

Page leant impressively across the table. 'You got something there. You know what Lady Astor said in Parliament? – That every man-jack serving out in the East should have to wear a yellow badge when he got back to the Blight.'

'What, officers and all?' Enoch asked.

'No, you North Country twirp, not officers – squaddies! In case they had the pox.'

'And Churchill backed her up, I bet. She and him are thick as thieves. She's in and out of Chequers as if it was her own back yard! Do you think Churchill gives a shite for the Fourteenth Army?'

For once Wally looked disconcerted.

'I reckon they've written us off, back home, that's true.'

' 'Course they have – anyone'll tell you! You ask some of the blokes as walked out of Mandalay – they'll tell you. That's why they pinched all our landing craft! We're the Forgotten Army!'

There was the magic phrase, gaining by constant repetition, which held so many easy bitternesses: The Forgotten Army. Dwelling on our hard life, we left my evening adventure safely behind.

The canteen was filling up now. More of the squad crowded in at our table, easing their beer glasses through the crush and lighting up cigarettes. Soon we were discussing once more the way our landing-craft had been withdrawn; it was regarded as almost a personal insult. Carter the Farter alone expressed a different opinion.

'It's nothing to do with India and Burma if they take the whole bloody Royal Navy away from this theatre of war. You bods don't understand that we've involved in an Imperialist War. They're gathering as many vessels as possible round Europe and then, when Hitler's beaten, the Allies will attack Russia – you'll see!'

Only Enoch admitted this was possible. The rest maintained that we were being victimized. It was all somehow India's fault; India was to blame for everything. So we were launched on the familiar subject of ants, snakes, shite-hawks, prickly-heat, and filth.

'It isn't as bad as all that!' I said.

'Fuck off, Stubbs, we know you're going bloody native!' Wally said. 'You'd rather be stationed in Kanchapur than London, you would!'

'I'd rather be stationed in Kanchapur than on fucking Salisbury Plain!'

Jeers and laughter drowned me out. I looked round for support. Old Bamber stood sombrely behind us, supping his beer and saying nothing, his sleeves rolled up to reveal the riot of tattooing on his arms.

'You could be in worse places than Kanchapur, Bammy, couldn't you?'

'All countries are the bloody same,' he said. 'There ain't no difference between them, once you really gets to know them. It don't matter where you are. One place is just like another.'

But to most of us without Bamber's experience it mattered extremely where we were.

Rumours and fears stirred like dust in the camp. 'Soon you will be leaving, sahib,' Ali told me as I bought my morning mug of *char* from him. 'Six day, maybe seven, all men go and new intake come Kanchapur.'

'I thought we were seeing the war out right here! Where are we going, Ali?'

'Japanese very bad man, sah'b, all the while eat very much land, kill good men with the rifle and the bayonet. Mendip Regiment go stop them not come in India, kill all person all the same.'

'Burma? Are you sure?'

'Yes, sah'b. All Mendip go Burma land, kill Japanese soldier. You owe me Ali one rupee six, sah'b.'

'I'll pay you on Friday, Ali.'

'Yes, sah'b, thank you, sah'b – then no more credit. Credit pinish.'

So I went to see Captain Gore-Blakeley and applied for a refresher course in wireless-operating. I caught him at a bad moment, as he was leaving the company office.

'Bit late for a refresher course, Stubbs, isn't it? We may be moving into action soon, you realize that, I suppose, eh? Don't want to be left behind, do you?'

'Of course not, sir.' Virtuously.

'Not that anyone is going to be left behind.' Off-handedly.

He moved into the intense sunlight, turning his back to me, but I tagged along.

'Your record is not one of the best, Stubbs.' Discouragingly.

'Ah, well, you see, that's just it, isn't it, sir?' Improvisingly.

'How do you mean, "That's just it"?' Disinterestedly.

'Well, sir, I mean I've had a run of bad luck, sir, losing

my stripes and all that. Now we're on Overseas Service, sir, I want to pull myself together and make something of myself. I am a Regular, sir. I thought if there was a quick refresher course in New Delhi or somewhere. . . .' Modestly.

'You're not stupid, are you, Stubbs?' Insultingly.

'Sir?' Insultingly.

'You aren't planning to become a proper wireless operator or anything, are you?' Coldly. We were moving across the parade ground; I was swinging my arms a bit and looking ahead with chin up in the approved manner, and finding it a ridiculous attitude in which to conduct a conversation. There seemed no suitable answer to his question except to say again, 'Sir?' I injected a note of keenness into it, to be on the safe side.

'I'll see what I can do for you, Stubbs, but you understand I can promise nothing.' Surprisingly.

'Thank you, sir.' Surprisedly.

'Fall out.' Inscrutably.

'Sir.' With a suitable dying fall.

I visualized myself in New Delhi, taking a long course by day, living with a beautiful and rich Indian girl by night, learning the language, assimilating the whole way of life – and of course getting stuck in every day. India was so vast, so complex – perhaps it would be possible, even for Army personnel, to disappear from mortal view into the life-enriching stews of its cities.

So I hoped, so I dreamed.

The gloomy fantasies of Stalin, the grandiose aspirations of Churchill, the calculations of Generalissimo Chiang Kai-shek, had fluttered down through the lists to us, serving time in Kanchapur. They had clobbered our amphibious plan. Yet, even without such a set-back, the Army could always operate under a system specially designed to annihilate anyone's time-sense. It punctuated long periods of inertia with sudden frenzied activity, in which everything had to be done – or half-done – in the shortest possible time.

You get switched from slow motion into rapid motion, and that was what happened to us in Kanchapur, half-way through March. Perhaps the Generalissimo had a bad night's sleep. As a result of these switches, you don't know – as the poetical phrase has it – whether it's arsehole or breakfast time. Such is the advantage of the system, since what you are doing is generally insufferable by normal time standards.

Our days were measured out in cigarettes, half-smoked cigarettes, football games, and visits to the NAAFI, while we waited in the heat for everything to burst apart and be different. The lists were coming home to roost. And the Japanese were preparing their March on Delhi.

We kept fitting in one more visit to the canteen.

I was coming out of the canteen with Geordie when the wheels began to grind again. Geordie was telling me some complicated and inarticulate story about his and his father's adventures in the Vickers engineering works in Newcastle, where he worked as a clerk, when he interrupted himself.

'Hello, here comes trouble! I'd better push off, mate – you won't want me. Here's the sergeant-major with invisible stripes, your friend and my friend – Jock McGuffie!'

This was said loud enough so that Jock, coming towards us with the brisk march he reserved for public places, could catch the gist of it.

'Aye, well, why aren't you young soldiers on parade or away blancoing your equipment? Ye'll get no promotion if you spend all your time boozing away in the canteen, young Geordie, I can tell you that. Now, do you mind if I have a wee word in the ear of Stubbs, here?'

'Taking him off on another of your sort of whorehouse-bashings, Jock?'

'Ock, away to your mither's breasts, sonny boy!'

Geordie nodded unhappily to me and walked off. Since communication was strictly codified, major meaning was conveyed non-verbally. The form of exchange between Jock and Geordie was entirely traditional, like so many of our exchanges; you took the meaning from the tone of voice and, more importantly, facial expression and gestures – they were what determined whether the intention was friendly or hostile. Geordie was definitely hostile to Jock – as far as he was definite about anything – while Jock could never be said to be friendly to anyone in any ordinary sense of the word.

There were indications, now that Geordie was heading towards barracks, that Jock was under emotional strain. He gripped my arm and looked up into my face.

'The bastards, the fucking mean scab-devouring mankey-minded shower of mother-fuckers! They're all for their fucking selves and no bloody mistake! I'll do *them*, I'm telling you! –'

'What's happened, Jock?'

'What's happened? What's happened? They've only turned down your application, that's what's happened!'

'What application?'

'Christ-on-fucking-crutches!' He clutched his ginger skull in dismay. 'What fucking application, he asks! *Your* application, man! Your application to go on a Radio Operator's course in New Delhi, that's what application.'

'That! I never thought that would come off. Gor-Blimey told me –'

'Yon bugger! Fucking Spunk Bucket! Look, mate, he could have pushed that application through if he had tried, you mark my words! Dodgey bastard! I'm going to *fix* him for you, you see if I don't!'

I laughed. 'Come on, Jock, I'll buy you a drink.' I made a gesture towards the canteen.

'No, I'm not going in there, there's someone as hates my fucking guts in there. We'll go over to the Q stores and see my old mate, Norm – he'll have a drink for us sure enough. But I'll get even with Gore-Bastarding-Blakeley, I'll fix him good and proper –'

As we moved towards the Q stores – I reluctantly, for I had detested the round-shouldered Corporal Norman since our first encounter – I said, 'I didn't expect the application to come off. Gor-Blimey warned me it probably wouldn't. Burma calls, Jock, old lad, and it's too late to get out of it now – we should have thought of that in England!'

His eyes narrowed. He went very cool and sinister. 'Rely on Jock McGuffie . . . Rely on Jock McGuffie. . . . That's all I say! Stick by him, he'll stick by you. We'll get ourselves out of this yet. But by God, if I could have driven you to New Delhi, they'd never have seen us for dust!'

'You'd got it all planned, then!'

''Course I'd got it all planned – what d'you take me for, a flaming idiot?' We were coming to the Q stores now, and he led round the back, always with his own guarded air, as if alert for ambush. 'But I've got other plans, you know that? Ay, other plans . . . There's a mucker of mine up at Division, and I'll be away to see him this evening. He'll help me with a little idea I'm working on. Never fear, laddie – we'll get even with all those wey-faced bullshitting. . . .'

His voice sank to a scurrilous hum. We walked forward into the building, our eyes adjusting to the dimness. The stores was a small warehouse choked with shelves and lockers, and tiny rooms made out of lockers and shelves, where everything from bales of barbed wire to heavy winter woollen underpants unfit for tropical use were piled, in the type of order peculiar to the Army: that is, alphabetically, so that bags, kit, universal; blankets, barrack; blouses, battledress, serge; boots, ankle; bowls, washing, enamel; braces, trousers for, pairs of; buckets, fire, iron; buckets, assorted; and burgees, marking, large and small, were all to be seen piled in one grey corner, despite their natural antipathy for one another.

In the middle of this three-dimensional excess of spelling, Corp Phil Norman, known as Norm, had his being; and the smell of his permanently burning fags could be traced to a cubbyhole where, snug among masks, dust; masks, eye; and mats, fibre; on the one hand, and sheets, waterproof; and shirts, bush; in various sizes on the other, he lived, slept and entertained his friends.

As Jock and I moved towards the front of the stores, picking our way along an aisle where an Indian orderly was arranging kit in lockers, we came upon Norm. He stood at the 'shun, his pale eyes looking meekly upwards at – none other than Captain Eric Gore-Blakeley himself.

'Yes, sir, yes, sir!', he was saying smartly, interrupting himself to cry to the orderly, 'Ali, don't slack off, now, get all them vests bundled up proper-like!' Then again, 'Yes, sir, yes, sir!'

To a certain extent horrified at the presence of any officer, and our platoon commander in particular, I turned to check on Jock's reaction. He was retreating fast, signalling to me, signalling to Norm over Gore-Blakeley's shoulder, contorting his face into extraordinary caricatures of warning (to me), hatred of officialdom (to Norm) and devotion to military discipline (to the Captain's back). At this moment, Gor-Blimey turned and saw us; the devotion-to-military-discipline expression became frozen on Jock's face while, in mid-step, he changed from a fugitive about to scram through the rear door to a soldier advancing to salute his superior officer.

'Sorry to interrupt, sir, I was just coming to see Corporal Norman about a bit of transport business, sir.' He marched past me and stood before Gor-Blimey, who surveyed him without pleasure – not that I had ever seen Gor-Blimey survey anyone with pleasure. I sprang to attention behind McGuffie, noting that his left hand was gesticulating to me behind his back.

'I wanted to see you, McGuffie.'

'Sir. I am here, sir.' He managed to contort his frame into an attitude of compliance while remaining at the 'shun.

'So I notice. It's about the non-delivery of a desk to the detachment at Indore. Your pigeon, I believe.'

'Desk, sir? Desk? Oh, yes, sir, the *metal* desk! Well, I can easily explain that, sir, you're quite right to complain about it – in fact I've been complaining about it myself, sir, only this morning, as it happens –'

Gor-Blimey's face looked as expressionless as those stone things on Easter Island. 'Right, well, I'll hear about that after tiffin, McGuffie. Report to my office before parade. Just now, I'm giving Corporal Norman instructions.'

'Ay, I quite understand, sir. No offence, sir, but I'm a bit busy myself just now –'

'Dismiss!'

McGuffie saluted smartly and turned, giving me ferocious grimaces as he passed. I interpreted them as meaning I should retreat too – which was quick of me, since I was partly preoccupied with the way Jock, in addressing the captain, had anglicized his voice, using an expression like "just now", where normally he would have said something sounding like 'th' noo'.

As I was also turning to go, Captain Gore-Blakeley said, 'Stubbs, I want you!'

'Sir!'

'Stand at ease.' I stood there while he resumed his talk with Norm. It was a technical discussion to do with kit inventories and kit surpluses in which I took no interest, beyond noting that Norm had now relaxed so much that a lighted stump of fag appeared in his hand as he and the captain bent over their lists. The mention of Rear Baggage Party made me listen more closely. Norm was part of Kanchapur's permanent cadre; he would be responsible for seeing that our company moved forward with stores up to strength.

'. . . We can leave that aspect to the sergeant-major,' Gor-Blimey was saying. 'And I want Stubbs in the rear detail. The C.O. thinks he should be given the chance to get his stripes back.'

He turned abruptly to me and said, 'Stubbs, since we are to be moving into action pretty soon, your application for refresher course has been turned down by Brigade H.Q. All courses are cancelled w.e.f. date, throughout the division.'

'Sir.'

'Will you be moving straight into action, sir, do you know?', Norm asked.

'It is pretty common knowledge that 2 Div, which is at present spread all over the sub-continent, is moving eastwards towards the catchment areas.'

'I suppose 2 Div will be heading for the Arakan, sir.' Norm said this in a tone implying that Gor-Blimey had a master plan in mind.

'That is not for me to say.'

'Oh, of course not, sir. It's a terrible country to fight in, is the Arakan, terrible country. The White Man's Grave.'

'The Fourteenth Army is trained to fight anywhere.'

'Of course it is, sir. Unfortunately, the Japs are too.'

Gore-Blakeley, who had been showing off his inflexibility of mind by maintaining this side-conversation without removing his gaze from me, now said to me, as if Norm had vanished, 'If we all come out of Burma intact, I suggest you re-apply for an operator's course then.'

Directly he took his attention from Norm, the latter –

having squeezed a precious drop of information for himself –
did vanish, fading into the recesses of his drab emporium as
if he had never been.

'Yes, sir.'

'Don't get involved in any more fights, Stubbs. You'll be
able to exercise your warlike spirit in Burma now.'

'Sir, I don't believe I have a warlike spirit.'

'Nonsense, man, don't argue! There's a touch of non-
conformity in you, isn't there, Stubbs?'

'Sir?'

'I've seen those pictures above your bunk, those gruesome
Hindu gods.'

There wasn't much I could say to this. We let his statement
lie between us, undisturbed apart from the shuffling movements of the Indian orderly, who was pushing boxes of
badges, regimental, along shelves. Most of us had pictures
above our beds, mainly girls, cut from the *Daily Mirror* or
Lilliput or *Razzle*; they were standard wanking-pit equipment,
as the phrase went. Among my nudes lurked the Monkey
God and other evil deities which not all the platoon's jibes
had induced me to take down.

'Are you interested in Hindu gods, Stubbs?'

'I s'pose I am, sort of, sir'. I was as adept in my way as
McGuffie in adopting the current idiom.

Gor-Blimey just stared at me, then said, 'I shall be in
charge of rear detail when we move out of Kanchapur. A
signaller might be needed. You'll come under Corporal
Dutt. Okay? Your name will come up on Orders in a day
or so.'

'Very good, sir.' Christ!

He was making to go. Norm emerged from the shadows,
pinching out an inch of cigarette as he came.

'If I might make a suggestion, sir, since I've seen many a
rear detail leave here and sometimes kit getting lifted – you
know how it is, sir. It might help to have a good reliable

driver i/c the M/T move. Perhaps I might suggest Driver McGuffie, who's proved his worth.'

'How reliable is he?'

'Oh, he's very *reliable*, sir, and of course he knows everyone.'

'Well, I'll be speaking to him this afternoon.'

'Thank you, sir! I'll leave it in your hands, then.'

Gor-Blimey left after the usual cascade of salutes. Norm nodded to me superciliously. 'It was touch-and-go there then!' By screwing his head round to one side, he managed to light up his inch of cigarette without burning his nose.

'How do you mean?'

'What I say – it was touch-and-go there for a minute! I thought the bugger was after your ring. I wouldn't trust him further than what I could throw him.'

'Piss off!'

'Don't you tell me to piss off, mate! You've been busted, and don't you forget it.'

'I'll bust your fucking nose!'

He pointed a yellowed finger to his stripes. 'What do you you think these are, then? Scotch mist? Look, mate, I've got nothing against you but you want to get some service in. I thought Jock was a mate of yours?'

'What if he is?'

'Well, then, you want to speak up for your mates, don't you? The way I did. If you want to get on in this man's Army, you got to know who your mates are and stick by them, and never mind all the rest of the shower.'

'I'll remember what you say.'

He had now sidled behind his counter and stood there with his hands resting on it, blowing smoke from his morsel of cigarette.

'I'll tell you summink else. You want to watch your step with me, or you'll be in trouble, see?'

At that particular moment, my inclination was to get out of

the stores and enjoy a breath of air unflavoured by old denims.

'I'm not looking for trouble! I came in here perfectly friendly with Jock, didn't I? What are you getting so snooty for? You were sucking up to officers a couple of minutes ago.'

'This place is out of bounds, you know that? Except to my mates. Another thing, you call me Corporal, get it? You want to watch your step with me, mate, 'cos I can be a bit dodgey at times, like. I've got a lot of friends round this camp, more than what you might think, see? What did Jock want, anyhow?'

'Something about a mate of his at Div, I believe.'

'What mate at Div?'

'He didn't happen to tell me. All right if I go now?'

He took the fag out of his mouth and rubbed his nose with a knuckle. 'What are you waiting for?'

You could tell the real regular soldiers, I thought. They formed an army within an army. People like McGuffie and the detestable Norm, and Rusk in the cookhouse were regulars by temperament. Conscripts like Wally Page and Enoch and Geordie were mere innocents by comparison. It was much like old lags versus first offenders in prison.

The lists were coming home, like rooks in evening light. Our prison was altering shape, propelling us towards Burma and the fighting for which we had been trained. Ali confirmed it: 'You go Calcutta first, sah'b, then across the Bramaputra River to the Burma Land.' But Ali had been making similar noises for some weeks.

The atmosphere in the barracks changed slightly. We could hear the jungle noises from the East. They made our last few days in Kanchapur unreal.

I managed a letter home. I walked alone near Kanchapur,

making one or two crude landscape sketches on a signals message pad – the relic of a craft I had learnt mainly for Veronica's sake. I played football, drank, laughed, swore, determined to have one last woman before we went into action and all got blown to bits.

The nightly piss-ups grew more riotous, the morning runs more strenuous. On the last night but one before the main force moved out of Kanchapur, I was almost flat broke, and went down to the Vaudette with Aylmer and Geordie to sit in the four anna seats and watch Humphrey Bogart in 'Casablanca', a Warner Brothers film; Warner Brothers were then my favourite studio, because they had Ida Lupino on the payroll.

We came out afterwards into the vivid twilight, Geordie discordantly whistling the theme song of the film, which necessitated a lot of manoeuvring of his Adam's apple. I was trying to see if we could muster enough cash between us for three beers. And what was Aylmer singing? – Under his breath, his old fragment of unfinished song: 'Could I but see thee stand before me. . . .'

'What is that fucking thing you keep singing?' Geordie asked, breaching an unwritten Army law of privacy.

'Just something my wife used to like, like,' Aylmer said dismissively.

'You never told us you were married!' I said.

'She died two and a-half years ago, in the Blitz. Get me pissed one night, and I'll tell you all about it.'

We turned into our favourite café and found a corner table. I was marvelling inwardly to think of Aylmer married. Marriage in those days seemed so far beyond me. Although – how long ago that was – I had proposed marriage to my darling Virginia – I was unable to imagine what it would be like to sustain a long relationship with a woman. How enviable it sounded: but would I be up to it?

'The Blitz was a bugger,' said Geordie, as we ordered

three beers on the strength of his last rupee. 'I don't reckon we ought to let up on the Germans until we've sort of flattened every one of their cities, the way they did London, like. It's just my personal opinion, of course.'

'One good thing about Burma – at least neither the Japs nor us have got any bastarding planes worth speaking about.'

'You're right there. What have we got? One lousy squadron of Spitfires!'

'Isn't it two by now?'

'You're in the Forgotten Army, mate, and don't you forget it!'

'That's right, the Forgotten Army – Britain's bloody Foreign Legion.'

'That's it – Join the Army and See the World!'

'I didn't bargain on having to *march* the fucker, too!'

While Geordie and I thus pleasantly rolled the conversational ball back and forth, we were drinking up and Aylmer was not saying much. All three of us were smoking like troopers, the waiters were doubling about the room, a fan was blowing warm air on us, and all told it was a pleasant evening. We were completely shut off from India, but by now I had begun to take that for granted.

'You don't know what the Blitz was really like,' Aylmer said. 'I was stationed in Hyde Park – I saw it all. I could tell you some terrible tales. . . . It's amazing what one lot of people will do to another. Like savages!'

Geordie said, 'Sergeant Meadow's house got blown up in the Blitz. Too bad he wasn't in it.'

'That's nothing. I knew a bloke – I knew a bloke got circumcised from a bomb.'

Geordie and I burst into laughter. We roared and shook and creased up over our beer. We went red in the face and wept. We sobered down, looked at each other, and burst into laughter again. It wasn't often Geordie laughed so much.

'Don't be so fucking wet! I'm telling you the truth,'

[151]

Aylmer said. 'He was circumcised by a bloody bomb. It was in a pub in Bermondsey, The Lamb. He was drinking in the public bar with his mates, see, and he thought he'd go and take a slash, like. This was near closing-time one evening. So he goes into the Gents and he's standing there having a pee and suddenly – boom! – the whole wall in front of him just caves in with nothing but blackness in front of him – still peeing, mind you!'

At the thought of this, we all three burst into laughter, until Aylmer went on. 'Of course, he was pretty shattered because he never even heard the bomb coming down. And he looks down at his prick to find it's bleeding as well as peeing. See, a bit of flying glass from the window cut his foreskin off as neat as a whistle – otherwise, he was completely okay!'

We were laughing, but I was not entirely comfortable; at this period I had not outgrown my resentment at my own circumcision. Every time I looked at that self-evident knob, I felt that some subtle quality had been lost.

'I've never understood why they circumcised anyone,' I said.

'Christ was circumcised,' Geordie said. 'They've still got his foreskin in the Vatican. I remember a bloke in the factory, like, told me that.'

'Fuck off! Still there all these years? It would have rotted away!'

'Christ's foreskin doesn't rot. It's eternal, like him. Any road, the officials at the Vatican keep it in a silver jug, like. So this bloke at the factory told me. I'm sure that's what he said. Pilgrims make special journeys to see it – you ask one of the R.C.s. If you're Christian, you're supposed to be circumcised, just like the Jews.'

'Jews aren't Christian.'

'They're sort of Christian. Aren't they sort of Christian, Jack? I don't know.'

'But even the Africans get circumcised, and they aren't Christians,' Aylmer said. He embarked on one of his histories, describing how the boys of African tribes were shut in special stockades for several months until the day of the ceremony, when the witch-doctor led them forth and did the deed. 'These are big lads – fifteen or sixteen, and their cocks bleed like pigs with slit throats. Some of them die after a day or two.'

'Bloody hell!', we said, and ordered more beer rapidly, pooling the rest of our cash on the table.

'The only real cure is to indulge in sexual intercourse at once with the women of the tribe. The juices of the vagina are healing, and if you're lucky you'll be okay after that. Else you bleed to death.'

'Dirty buggers!', Geordie said. 'People do terrible things to each other, when you come to think. . . .'

Next morning was the last day before the main party moved out of Kanchapur. The advance party under Captain Hale had already left.

As we returned from our pre-breakfast run, Geordie said, 'I thought like us were going to get Aylmer's story about how his wife was polished off by that bomb. You were a bit simple, weren't you, mucker, I mean? I thought we were going to get it again!'

'I've never heard it!'

'You want to get some service in, then, mate!'

'What happened to his wife, anyway?'

Geordie glared round the barrack-room, perhaps gathering his powers of narrative.

As we were stripping off our denims, he said, 'Oh, him and his missus had gone back to their digs – or a flat I think he said it was. Anyroad, they were a bit plastered like on the night this happened – he was on leave or something – I forget the details – and anyroad they went to bed and fell asleep like, and when he woke up the ceiling was coming in – falling down, I mean – and he fell asleep again or something because he was so pissed, and when he woke up in the morning, a bloody great beam had come down across the bed like, and his missus was dead beside him, squashed under the beam.'

He laughed.

'Poor sod! Enough to send anyone round the bend!'

We were grabbing up our mess-tins and eating irons – in Kanchapur, you were allowed to go down to mess hall half-dressed for breakfast.

'Aye, well, anyroad, he couldn't get the fucking beam off of her chest, no matter how hard he tugged, so he tried to get out through the door, and the door wouldn't open, like, or something, because, you see, what had happened – he didn't know it at the time – but what had happened, the blast from this bomb had blown the staircase away and jammed the door tight. So it *couldn't* open. So he says. So he calls out the window, but there's a bloody great crater outside – see, they try to bring a ladder, like, the neighbours or someone, but the crater's in the way, and the fire engine can't get because of the rubble. Fuck off, Page!'

This was said to Wally, who ran up and grabbed us as we were going down the stairs, dealing us both a swift pummel on the upper arm.

'Is he giving you a lot of shit, Stubby? You want to do the bastard – he's always gripping is our Wilkinson!'

'Why don't you shut your arse and give your mouth a chance, Page?'

'He was telling me about Aylmer and his missus, when she was killed by the bomb.'

'Oh, that! Fucking wrap up! – You'd think old Jack was the only bloke what ever had his old woman die on him!'

[154]

'Get on with it, then, Geordie, for fuck's sake! What happened to him up in his bedroom?'

'Nothing much,' Geordie said, as we clanked into the mess room and moved to join the queue of men waiting for Rusk to wield his ladle. He looked round, trying to re-grasp the thread of story. 'He was stuck up in the bedroom all day, like, with his dead missus all bloody on the bed. He nearly went off his nut, according to him. It started raining or something, see, near midday or some time, with the rain come in the ceiling like, because the roof had been blown off by this bloody great bomb, so he spent all his time till they rescued him trying to keep the rain off her mush. I may have got a few details wrong . . .'

'Ywwr, bet he had one last bunk-up before they carted her away,' Page said. 'Dirty bastard. . .'

After the dollop of bergoo, it was bacon and soya-link, as usual: the diet of the Forgotten Army.

Love and death – how we laughed about them! Yet they made the rest of the business look pretty pale. All the incidentals of that day, occupied by packing up and throwing out, were bleached by them, as if by strong sunlight.

While throwing out old copies of *Picturegoer*, *Leader* and *Picture Post* – sent from home by my sister – I thought about leaving India. Had we ever been in India? It was a travesty! Here was the setting for a towering love affair, complete with mighty vegetation and ugly shadows – a country where love, *Love*, could reach a pitch unknown in the pallid UK climate: yet no lover presented herself. Women here went about in dreadful disguises, made-up as whores in rags or officers' memsahibs in pleated tennis-skirts. And all forbidden!

In Burma or Assam, all that sort of thing would be out.

[155]

War. Even the imagining of love would have to be put away. Nor even Jock McGuffie, with his mad schemes for dodging the column, could save me then.

There are times in a man's life when he is preoccupied almost continually with the promptings of his cock. Those are the times when he should be able to follow the direction in which it points and find out how the pulse of the world beats.

What had there been instead? A couple of quick sniffs inside filthy brothels, and a hell of a lot too much bishop-bashing. I was tearing myself apart, like the Monkey God.

The C.O. of Kanchapur spoke to us on passing-out parade, neat, heavy, anonymous, standing immobile in the shade while we sweated immobile in the sun to listen to him.

'... You have acquitted yourselves well. You must be proud to know that you are now fully trained fighting-machines. Your training in combined operations has not been wasted. It has given you experience of any conditions you are likely to meet in Burma or Assam. You have been a splendid body of men to train, well worthy of the division to which you belong, well worthy of the objective for which you have been trained: the Liberation of Burma from the Japanese. And I only wish I was coming with you. . .'

'You can have my fucking place, for one.' That was Dusty Miller.

'No talking in the ranks,' Charley Meadows said.

Perhaps I hoped that McGuffie's poison was an antidote to the poison of the Army. All these years later, I do not recall what I believed. I can look back on that young Horatio with the same amazement that I then felt for my fellow men.

So it was to McGuffie, down in the scruffy M/T Section, that I went when the day was over. He seemed to believe still that some amazing trick could be pulled which would save those of us on rear detail from getting farther east than Calcutta; so glib was he about this, I partly believed him. But first there was our last evening in Kanchapur.

'Och, what you wanne go to Indore for, you dirty lecherous Sassenach? Them mankey whores in yon knocking-shop'll give you a dose as soon as look at you. There's no' a one of them as isn't rotten with siff. It's no' my place to lead a young lad like you into temptation, Stubby! – Besides, the fucking Redcaps would have my guts for garters if they could.'

'Come on, Jock, you'll be telling me next to stick to the old five-fingered widow, the way the rest of the old soldiers do!'

'Aye, weel, she'll no' do you much good eether in this fucking stinking climate. It's no' a place for a white man. We've got fucking Churchill to thank for all this, sending us out to this bloody dump. . . . Why not go over to Indore while we're still in the land of the fucking living? At least we can get boozed up.'

'I promised young Jackie Tertis I'd take him along to a whorehouse some time. Is it *thik-hai* if he comes too?'

'Christ, man, we don't want bairns along! Tertis is as bad as yon Geordie mucker of yours. If you want to go to Indore, let's *go* to Indore – not muck about wi' a Sunday School. Besides, I've still got yon office desk to deliver . . . Gore-Blakeley gave me a right bollocking about it.'

So to Indore we went, bumping over the lousy roads through the steaming purple night, and with beating heart I again found myself climbing the stairs up to that ill-lit landing in the knocking-shop. Life continued here as before, had continued here for – how long? Day and night, fucking in the cubicles and domestic conversation just outside. The two old crones were still working at their chores, one hunched over a sewing-machine, cranking away and barely glancing up as Jock and I rather drunkenly gained the landing. We had visited his friend in the hotel down the street.

'Mebbe tonight I'll give the old granny an airing,' Jock said, pointing to the crone working the sewing-machine.

Beside the old granny stood a girl of about eight, shy and quiet and pretty, peeping at us. The hag in charge appeared and we began to argue about money, while the little girl watched.

I was befuddled and angry. I began to shout and wave my fists about. The hag was saying something I could not understand, stroking my arm to soothe me. The gesture maddened me more. I yelled at her not to paw me. A man in creased white trousers came up the stairs and stood about inconspicuously.

Eventually Jock cooled her and me down. We went through to the room we had visited before. It looked as ever, a long stuffy room, cluttered and dark – perhaps never lit except by the cheesy glow of a lamp in the street, which did little more than make the window-panes shine like clouds.

A woman rose up from a bed, a dark silhouette.

'Hello, sweetheart!'

'Hello – who are you?'

'Hello, sweetheart. You like jig-jig?'

'I want a look at you first.'

I grabbed hold of her – at least I was touching a woman, however loathesome she might be. Was it the same one I had grappled with before? I felt incredibly pissed and not in the mood to be fucked about.

I smacked her to keep her quiet.

She was wearing an ankle-length garment, perhaps an old nightdress. I stuck my hand up it and felt a crisp knot of pubic hair. Immediately, something in me realized its intentions, and my prick struggled erect inside my trousers. I got the woman down on the bed – no hesitations this time about how filthy it might be – and half-knelt beside her, feeling for matches in my pocket with one hand, while holding her down with the other. She was struggling. I would stand no nonsense. We were off tomorrow.

I got the matches out, let go of the *bibi*, struck one. She cried out and slapped at the light before it had a chance to grow. Swearing, I tried to light another. They were wretched Indian matches – one in three was a dud. Someone was behind me, trying to stop me striking a light.

'No, sir, you disturb other customer make jig-jig!'

'I want a fucking dekko! Let me alone!'

Elbowing them off, I got a match alight and stared down at the woman I had paid for. She stopped writhing as the light fell on her, merely putting her hands up defensively, so that their shadows fell across her face in bars. I dragged her hands away.

She was young, her teeth were white, her skin smooth! I let the match die and lay down beside her, catching the smell of her as I tore my trousers off. My hands ran over her plump arms, over her body. I could hear myself groaning, while the hag by the bedside was trying to get two rupees off me for a french letter. Cursing, I gave her two half-rupee pieces and told her to fuck off.

The girl's body was slightly oily. She was co-operating now. I inhaled its odours, natural and artificial, letting the musky smell work down to my parched roots while my fingers probed into her hot, tacky little crutch. She peeled the french letter on to my weapon in a prosaic housewifely manner while I – in what animal past was I, tunnelling through a dense familiar element, triumphant, cock-a-hoop?

When you're having a shag, you must be in touch with all your ancestors right back to the Jurassic. It's *the* moment – an escape into all the imagined freedoms of past matings. This girl wrapped her legs round me like a stone-age lass, and pummelled me with her heels on my bum as I shot my row with considerable force and splendour into what was probably a secondhand french letter.

She got up at once and started fiddling with something she dragged from under the bed – a towel or a rag. Her business was over, she had felt nothing. The deal was closed. And we were off in the morning!

She was really quite young and pretty. Suddenly I remembered the last night of my embarkation leave, when I'd nearly managed a knee-trembler with Our Syl in the air-raid shelter. It came back to me clear as could be – and how I had failed to get my oats.

'I'm going to bloody have you again!' I said. I grabbed the towel from her, pulled her sari away, got her vest right up under her armpits. Then I could see her body in the cloudy light, shining like milk, her breasts and the narrow thighs. I kissed her on the lips. She struggled, but I held her head in my hands and kissed her, pressing my tongue into her mouth, forcing my body against hers.

My hard-on came swinging up again, red in tooth and claw, positively suppurating inside its french letter. I slid it in and had her against the wall, slap up against the cockroach stains. She made no protest as I thrust away, beyond avoiding my mouth. Perhaps the taste of beer and fags didn't appeal to her. I came almost as fast as I had done the first time, surging with joy. It was absolutely exhausting, and I collapsed on to the bed, my legs shaking, chuckling a bit.

'You're a good girl – good girl . . . *Boht acha bibi, malum?*' I was just about panting. So much for amphibious training!

She stood where she was, saying nothing. She pulled her vest down, waiting by the window.

'Don't be afraid. . .'

She put out her hand. 'Five rupee, Johnny. Give five rupee!'

The frenchie felt disgusting, I pulled it off and slung it

under the bed. My prick I wiped on my handkerchief. As I was dragging my trousers on, I heard Jock calling me.

'Coming, Jock!'

'Five rupee! Give me!'

'Sorry, sweetheart, I'm broke!'

'You give five rupee, sweetheart! Two rupee!'

On the landing, the little girl watched us as we went by. The old crone kept on stitching.

'Goo'-night!', I called to them grandly, feeling light-headed, no doubt because I'd got so much dirty water off my chest.

As we stumbled down the wooden stairs. I said to Jock, 'By Christ, I just about raped that fucking *bibi*!'

'Balls, man, ye canna rape any woman ye find in a knocking-shop! It's going against the laws of nature. Be your bloody age!'

Directly I woke next morning, the dread of syphilis was on me. To think I'd stuck my tongue into her dirty mouth! – That was what disgusted me most. 'Never kiss a whore!' I had often heard old Dave Feather say that. 'Do you what like with them, but never kiss their lips.'

I knew that I was doomed to go through that routine of glancing at your prick every morning, scrutinizing it as it cowered in your palm, searching for spots, sores, pus, imagining the whole thing as diseased as the loathesome knobs on the posters the authorities stuck up in shithouses.

Meanwhile, all my innocent mates were humping their packs on. It was 17 March, and at last the Mendips were leaving Kanchapur behind them.

'Honey pears! I've had enough of square-bashing! Lead me to the Japs!' Enoch cried.

'Hope we see you again soon, mate,' Geordie said, his

Adam's apple bobbing with the emotion he was never quite up to expressing.

'Don't worry, Stubby, me old mucker! You'll be catching us up soon,' Wally said, giving me one last affectionate bash on the biceps. 'My slit-trench is the first on the right, next to the cookhouse. Cheerio, Ali, you old robber!'

'Good-bye, sah'b! Come back to Kanchapur when you kill all the Japanese soldier, have some more tea for to drink!' Ali managed to look genuinely sorry to see us go.

Bamber, the old lag, clapped me on the shoulder. 'Chin up, Stubbs, me lad. Remember – when you're travelling, you ain't doing anything worse!' This was a sort of catch phrase of his, which we all enjoyed quoting.

What a lot of good bods they were! We were all in the shit together and it was madness to try and escape it. Much better to die together, if necessary!

Charley Cox came up with Dusty Miller. They would soon be manning the Bren gun together.

'We'll drop you a card when we get there, Stubby!'

'Fuck off, we'll only be four days behind you, doing all the dirty work as usual.'

'That's all right for you,' Dusty said, 'but we don't even know where we're going for sure, do we, Charley?'

'We're going to Calcutta, but we shan't get much chance to stay there, worse luck. We might be sent to Chittagong – some of 2 Div is there. Or we might go north. Depends where they want us in Burma – in the Arakan or somewhere else. Who knows, perhaps they've found up a few LCTs for us that didn't get sent to the Mediterranean! Seeing that the Japs are now closing in on Imphal, we might get sent there – or Kohima, which used to be quite a nice little peace-time station.'

That was the first time I heard Kohima mentioned as a possible destination.

Dusty Miller swung his kit-bag on to his shoulder and

said, 'Look, Stubby, here's a precious item for you – the
squad copy of *Micheal Meatyard*. Best book ever written after
the Bible! I can't get it in my kit, so you'd better hang onto
it!'

'The bastard will flog it,' Carter the Farter said.

'Oh, no, I won't! Not on your Nelly!'

Our kit-scale had been reduced. Without a qualm, I had
got rid of a whole kit-bag full of kit and personal possessions,
including my dress-hat in the Mendip colours, which I
presented to Ali. Perhaps it is still being worn in some un-
heard-of Indian village, to this very day. But *The Night
Times of Micheal Meatyard* was obviously too precious to be
discarded.

Pornography of the foulest and most laughable kind was
on sale everywhere in India. The Indians themselves seemed
hardly to distinguish between sex and venereal disease; their
bookshops had counters full of books on both subjects, as if
they could not tell the difference between erotic and anti-
erotic. Whenever I hear that the East is less muddled on the
subject of sex than the West, I remember all those filthy
books on V.D.

But *Micheal Meatyard*, with its liberating quota of mis-
prints and schoolboy's howler English, was more enjoyable,
and had provoked the flow of laughter as well as semen in
our barrack-block.

Micheal's twin eyes bruned like carbunkles as he bent
down naked in his shower to pear through the partition
that formed a dirision from his cousin Vera's anotomical
details. How monstrous the total curvaceousness of her
ample breasts and her belly swelling down to that divine
gully of her nether lips. It was all plainly revealed to
Micheal's scorching gazement, the huge organ of his
manhood began slowly to rear towards its full length,
when he felt at his rear a brutal thrust of the penetration
behind. Turning, it was none other than his fate to view

[163]

there Vera's father, his eveil uncle Herbert. In a depraved state clad only in a towel, his unwanted digit thrust mercilessly at him.

'If you want to lie with Vera,' he hissed, 'You must also lie with me.'

Micheal agrees to the deal, for by this point in his young life he has become accustomed to many outrageous couplings.

Who wrote the immortal *Micheal Meatyard*? Where was it written? Meatyard's antics must have delighted thousands of British troops. There was no clue to the author's nationality. The setting of the book was Venice, which may have meant only that the writer had read his Casanova. No use was made of the Venetian setting, unless one counts the early scene in the book where Micheal attends a masked ball. There he dances with a buxom matron, masked as he is; they become excited by each other and go to a nearby bedroom. Only when the lady opens her legs does Micheal recognize – his mother!

This is the first of a long series of incestuous encounters which become, step by step, more complicated and more unlikely. The climax of the story is a grand scene involving Micheal and thirteen of his relations, including Uncle Herbert and Cousin Vera, in which Grandma proves to be more insatiable than any of them except Micheal.

What has happened to that masterpiece of nonsense? Is it lost to the world? The chances seem good that at least one copy was brought back to the UK before the British finally quit India. I lost our platoon copy in some forgotten rifle-pit in Assam.

No bands were playing. The 1st Battalion of the Mendips climbed up into the fleet of lorries which was transporting it to the railway station at Indore. I stood in my denims

watching them drive through the main gate, with Aylmer
beside me.

'It's a brave sight,' he said. 'Now we're leaving this dump,
it seems no time since we arrived.'

Soon the place was empty. We went and loaded equipment in the midst of an unexpected solitude. Rear detail
would follow main party in four days, under Gor-Blimey.
The cadre was still about, but they had a habit of fading
away to their *charpoys* when there was work to be done, just
as Norm faded into the obscurity of his stores. At night there
was guard duty, and the nights were wider and wilder than
they ever were in England. There was plenty of time to
wonder what exactly was happening, and to come to no
conclusion.

It was best to stop feeling, as far as that was possible.
Army training was something of a help towards this end.
The working-class credo seemed also to be aimed in the
same direction; my mates generally gave an appearance of
cheer. What I regarded as a middle-class sinking feeling
was my monopoly – or was that a personal trait rather than a
class property? The real hope for the time ahead seemed to
be to become as rough and tough as possible and to live for
the moment. That was it – never think one day ahead, forget
consequences, travel blind, ignore V.D. warnings, be shit-or-
bust! Choose sex rather than love, if offered either – sex
was momentary; love endured, if only for a little time.

Christ, if only I could work out such distinctions in practice! A knocking-shop is no place in which to grow up . . . so
what would a battlefield be like?

Indore railway junction again, spread flat under the rolling
mills of mid-day heat, rails and engines and engine-sheds all
made of incandescent dust, painted over with black lead. We

[165]

climbed out of the lorries and the sight was familiar to us. Here we had climbed into lorries weeks before, fresh from Bombay and the boat, to head for the terrors of unknown Kanchapur. Then, in our solar *topees*, we had been no more than pink jelly in the hands of predatory porters; now, in our bush hats, we could repel the most persistent beggar with a stream of oaths and mangled Urdu.

We had been acclimatized. We had India in the bloodstream, with all its havoc and noise and age and decrepitude and beauty and decay – so thoroughly into the bloodstream, that in my case it lodged there like gravel in the kidney, playing me up from time to time.

We spent two days at the junction, supervising the loading of stores into the military bogies of our train, shouting at the welter of porters – all fingers, bare feet and flashing teeth – who jostled for the honour of bearing our burdens. The train stood in a desolate siding, a hundred yards or more from the lane where the vehicles parked. We picked our way back and forth across the tracks, tracks that led to incredible places with bizarre names. What could life be like in Quetta, Amritsa, Kuttack, Seringapatam, Chittagong, Vizagapatnam and Barrackpore? The latter at least might soon become more than a name, because to Barrackpore the main party was going before the final move into action. Barrackpore was hundreds of miles away, beyond Calcutta. It looked as if Ali's information was correct.

Little tank-engines moved slowly back and forth in the sidings, careful to avoid our line of porters. The drivers waved cheerfully to us. They could not actually love us, could they?

Evening. The sun went down behind a convenient engine shed. The great sleazy town stirred, lights came on, young fellows came out clutching newly washed dhotis to their crutches and spat *betel*-juice into the dust. The brothels would be opening – or did they ever close? Life and lights and terrible things began to feed on the night. We did spells of guard with fixed bayonets by the siding; when we were off guard, we kipped on one of the station platforms outside the RTO office, under our mozzy-nets.

To sleep on a railway platform! If my poor dear parents could have seen me, with the *char*-wallahs and the three-legged pye-dogs prowling by! I took the ten-till-midnight and the four-till-six shifts on guard, so securing the privilege, during my second watch, of seeing the sky lighten with dawn, heavy birds begin to fly, and the armed ranks of railway lines glitter towards me like naked bayonets.

Among the dozen or so of us on rear detail were Corporal Ernie Dutt, Jock McGuffie, Carter the Farter, Feather, Harding, Gillespie, and young Jackie Tertis. The station canteen opened at eight in the morning, and we all filed in for a breakfast of eggs-and-chips, bread and jam, cakes and tea.

'If yon's breakfast, roll on fucking dinner,' Jock said, swigging down the last of his tea. 'I see they've started us on half-rations already.'

'Shit in it, Jock, you're always bloody grumbling,' Dutt said. 'Let's start as we mean to go on.'

Jock put on his aggrieved-but-reasonable air. 'Somebody's got to complain round here, Ernie. May I remind you that they'll twist us for the last fucking brass farthing if you let them get away with it.' He began one of his stories of victimization in Glasgow from which, I knew, he would emerge victorious in the end.

Lighting a fag, I strolled out on to the platform. Tertis followed me.

'I'll be glad to get into action, Stubby, won't you? Better than hanging about. I'm not scared of a few Japs. Perhaps with a bit of action my cock'll go down. It drives me bloody mad, it does – I'm just wanking myself silly. I've only got to move and I get a touch of the duke. It's this bloody fucking heat, it's bad for you!'

'The Japs probably get the same trouble. When you get to Burma, you'll find the jungle's knee-deep in yellow semen.'

'So you slip up in it, like, you mean?' He burst into laughter. 'Pity any Burmese girl goes in there – she'd be up the spout in no time!' After a minute, he said, 'Old Jock McGuffie reckons he's not going to Burma, reckons he's got some personal feud against Gor-Blimey, and says he's got some tricks up his sleeve. What does he mean by that, do you think?'

'You never know what old Jock's up to.' A *chicko* came and begged for *baksheesh*. I waved him on. 'Jock's pretty deep.'

'So are you, Stubby, aren't you? I mean, you're pretty deep, aren't you? I reckon you know a thing or two – I've always said so!'

'Get your knees brown, young Tertis!'

'Here, Stubby, you said you'd take me to a brothel one day, remember? Do you remember what you said that other night? You know I'm dying for a bloody bit. You never took me, did you?'

'What about that girl of yours at home?'

'Oh, don't take the piss! When we get to Calcutta ... Hey, the blokes say Calcutta's got more whore-houses than it has shitters. How about it, Stubby, just you and me – I don't want your mate Jock coming along, 'cos he'd just laugh at me, wu'n't he, I mean, like?'

Three *chickos* stood nearby, watching us. One sidled forward and said to us in a bashful voice, 'You like gobble, Johnny? Nice sweet mouth opens only five rupee . . .'

He stood looking up at us. We stood looking down at him. Cheeky little bugger, half-grinning, a likely-looking lad. He could do it without having to stoop.

'Jackie,' I said, 'Now's your chance! Let this *chicko* have a suck of it!'

He was dithering and unhappy. Shall I? Shan't I? I'd be too ashamed! It was such a disgusting thing to do, he had to do something, he could not afford five chips . . .

'Four rupee, Johnny – both two men, seven rupee only, you pay me first, I no go away till job done proper, you like very much!' The *chicko* waggled his fingers to illustrate his maths.

'The lad's keen, Jackie – have a bash, it's your birthday!'

'Christ, I couldn't . . . Look, you come too, have one with me. I'll stand you a gobble.'

'Fuck off! I'd choke him! Knock him down to three rupees and it's a bargain.'

'Look, boy, you filthy little bastard, I'll give you two-and-a-half rupees, no more. *Malum*? Two rupee eight anna, *thik-hai*? Oh God, I never ought to do it! If my old man could see me! Where do we go, anyway? Suppose the Redcaps pick us up? What if someone caught us doing it?'

'Tell them you were having a pee and the *chicko* ran up and bit your knob in a fit of anti-British feeling!'

The *chicko* knew a push-over when he saw one; by now, he probably owns the biggest brothel east of Bombay. He grabbed Tertis's hand and started to pull him towards the back of the station, uttering words of reassurance and encouragement as they went. His pals acted as chorus in the background. Tertis looked despairingly at me.

'At least come and keep guard, Stubbs, you rotten fucker!'

I laughed and tapped my rifle. 'Shall I put one up the spout?'

But it was impossible not to feel sorry for him. He was so vulnerable. What the hell would he be like in action? Sheer Jap-fodder! At least he might as well enjoy a good gobble before getting killed.

The *chicko* took him to a corner in an angle between sheds and undid his flies without a moment's hesitation, darting his hand inside.

Tertis moaned. 'Don't look!' he said, his face forlorn and formless as it turned towards me. I had swung away instinctively. I kept watch while the *chicko* worked away and the *chicko*'s two friends stood and watched me, whispering and tittering to each other. No other figures were visible, except at a distance, ambling over waste ground. A screen of corrugated iron hid us from most of the junction.

The noises Tertis made provided a running commentary on the state of affairs, from his initial inability to get a hard-on to when he came his load – followed by immediate demands for cash and buckshees from the *chicko*. I got what Tertis called a touch of the duke myself, just listening. This was cured by frightful throat-clearings and spittings by the *chicko*, as he cleared out his mouth on the ashy dust, harsh sounds full of hatred.

'You're lucky he didn't munch the end off,' I said, as Tertis rejoined me, pale and sweating. He did not answer.

'*Tik-hai?*'

'You won't tell any fucker, will you? Not Jock nor nobody?'

We went back to the others in silence.

Throughout that day, the lorries came and went, and we supervised the loading of their contents into our train, gathering furnace-heat in its siding.

The last thing to be loaded was a sackful of rations, our food for the journey – cans of bully beef, jam, marmalade, American oleomargarine, fruit and condensed milk, as well as tea, sugar and bread. We left a guard on the train and the rest of us plunged into town for a quick look round and a drink. By six, we were back at the train, cheerful and relaxed, entirely independent of anything that might happen next.

Nothing happened for a long while. We talked about

football matches. Harding played a mouth organ. We recovered from the amazement of finding that Captain Gore-Blakeley, installed in the next carriage, had a compartment all to himself, whereas there were twelve in our compartment. As Dutt sensibly pointed out, 'We wouldn't want him in here with us.'

The sun set. Even the beggars had deserted us. The station lights went on, and the lights of the great decaying world. The macaque monkeys which lived in the sheds nearby and had watched our loading operations with interest were now settling for the night; they were stocky animals, agile, unsqualid, detached from their surroundings – the serviceman's final proof that India and Indians were barbarous. When the light failed, the monkeys scuttled away, we were alone in the sidings.

The Mendips were on to episodes from their life-histories now. They never pretended that living was other than a dreadful and on the whole makeshift thing, or that it couldn't be got through pretty well by anyone with a strong stomach and a sense of humour.

The captain poked his head in through our window.

'I've just been over to the RTO and departure time has been postponed for a few hours.' Groans from us all.

'The train will leave in the morning, as early as possible. It means you will have to sleep here. I'm sorry about that. Corporal Dutt, arrange a guard on the train as last night, two-on, four-off, right?'

'Yes, sir. Can those off duty sleep on the platform as last night?'

'I think it better you should all stay here. I'm sorry there's no lighting in the carriage. I shall be over at the RTO's all night, if you need me. I have laid on *char* for ten tonight. All straightforward?'

'Yessir!'

'Get as much sleep as you can.'

[171]

We burst into groans and curses as he left. Furious though we were, the element of surprise was lacking. Our unanimous verdict was that such delay and inconvenience were fucking typical.

Before morning came, we were stirring, jumping down and stretching, peeing against the carriage, having an early fag, calling to the monkeys. We straggled across the railway lines to the platforms for a shit and a shave and a bite of breakfast. Half-an-hour after it was up, the sun was tickling the backs of our necks with its heat.

The breakfast served on the station meant that we saved the rations in the sack. This sack stood on the wooden bench in our compartment, next to the open window. Feather and Carter the Farter and I were strolling back towards the train after breakfast. Jock McGuffie, as it happened, was the only one actually in the compartment. He gave an agonized cry as we were approaching.

'They fucking bastarding skiving monkeys!'

He appeared in the window brandishing a heavy machete.

We saw what had happened. The macaques had come along the roof of the train. Jock had been trying to tempt one into the compartment with a cigarette, perhaps intending to catch it. The monkeys had swarmed down – and one had grabbed two loaves of bread from our precious store.

I gave an answering yell, flung my rifle to Carter the Farter, and dashed forward. The robber-monkey was making off along the roof of the train, not going particularly fast, a loaf of bread under each arm. I jumped into the open doorway, put a foot up on the window-sill, and heaved myself on to the roof. The world looked different up there – a wider panorama of desolation.

Several monkeys were scrabbling about on the roof. They froze and looked at me reprovingly, with the scepticism reserved for an outsider. Perhaps they had their own ghastly society up there, a duplicate of the one below. I stood up and made a dash at the one who had appointed himself baker. At once, all were on the run.

It was exhilarating clonking along the carriages, jumping from one to the other, urged on by cheers from below. Some of the macaques dived to one side – off the train and on to the nearby sheds in splendid leaps. My boy ran towards the engine. He was not particularly putting himself out, and would occasionally look back over his shoulder in encouragement. He dropped one of the loaves of bread. It meant nothing to him.

He turned. He was going to jump off the train, and then he would be gone. Yelling, I gave a great leap forward. The steel on my boots skidded against a roofing stud. I slipped. He looked in astonishment at me as he sailed, loaf and all, across to a crumbling stone parapet. I was tumbling over the slope of the carriage roof, my hands out to stop myself. No luck. Over I went, head first. There were wires and messy iron things below, lying in the ash. I joined them.

They helped me back into the carriage. Someone retrieved the loaf the monkey had dropped. Feather brought me a mug of *char*. The Corp gave me a fag. Carter the Farter brought along a sweat-rag dipped in water with which I mopped at my face and hands. It felt as if I had broken my arm and both knee-caps.

'Give him some fucking air!' Jock said. 'The wee lad's fair laid out. Lie him down on the seat, flat out, lie him down on the seat! I've been in the same way myself many a time, and all you want's a wee bit air and a lie down and you're right again in no time! I'll kill those fucking monkeys, I will, I'll have their bloody guts for garters, I'll bite their balls off. We'll have you fighting fit again in no time, Stubbs, old laddie, dinna worry – give us a fucking fag, Corp, and let's make room for him along this fucking seat.'

'I'd better get the captain,' Corporal Dutt said.

'Och, there's no point in dragging that bugger in,' Jock said, with his instinctive unease at the mention of authority. 'Mebbe I'll just have a *shufti* in at the canteen and see if they've a loaf or two going spare. . . .'

'What sort of a country is this,' Carter the Farter said, 'Where the monkeys runs away with your basic rations like a lot of flaming Nig-Nogs?'

'That's where the Nig-Nogs come from, isn't it?' the Corp said. 'It's all in Darwin – one lot come out of the other.' He glanced out of the window accusingly as if, in that heat, the evolutionary process could be taking place again at any minute.

Although I appreciated their fuss, I was in no state to enjoy it. I lay on the seat as they desired, my head on a pack and the sweat-rag on my forehead, while pain chased up and down my legs and my right arm. What a bastard!

Towards mid-day, our train finally started its long journey east towards Calcutta. The breeze was welcome. Outside, a great bowl of plain cluttered by, eroded by a million years of sunshine. For no known reason, I was asking myself how anyone could be expected to have any character in such a setting. The plain and the sun between them ground down to dust any possibility that individual lives were significant.

We had periodic glimpses of skeletal farmers immobile on the plain, grazing it with ploughs dragged by wafer-thin oxen. How could one imagine those farmers had – in any English sense – character? "Circumstance is more than character": where had I heard that? I was having enough trouble trying to establish my own character. Even when I got away from this terrifying land, if I ever did, it might prove impossible to forget the plain and the sun and the mental deserts they represented. What a bastard it all was!

Everything was in balance in my mind, as I drifted in a
light delirium. The tent of my life had three pegs to it: my
upbringing, the Army and India. The poor flapping canvas
between was out of control.

Jock McGuffie was prodding me.

'Hey, Stubby, you're making a beast of yourself with this
fucking wooden seat, so-called. How about sitting up now
you're feeling better and letting some of your mates rest their
arses a wee bitty?'

What had I been thinking about? The daydream had
gone. I shifted up a bit while the rest of them settled down
to a game of pontoon.

It's beyond me to describe what Calcutta was like. I had no
adequate terms of reference for it then, nor am I sure I have
now, a quarter-of-a-century later. Time-lapses are not always a help. All I see, looking back not just to Calcutta but
to the time of war in the Forties, are scenes diminished
by perspective – still bright, but shrunken by all the changes
since. Despite myself, I'm writing history. The honest truth
is, I don't remember what it was like to be Private Stubbs,
although I remember the things he did. It is not only times
that change; human character is even less stable than we
care to think, and alters out of recognition under the impact
of the years, like a boxer's ear.

So all you can say about Calcutta is that it was the
capital city of the impoverished world. Inside its tattered
confines, hardship, suffering, and degradation were so busy
that they made Victorian London seem like the City of the
Blessed. The refugees from the surrounding countryside –
which at that time was locked in famine – imported their
particular stone-age poverty to the worn-out streets. I had
written proudly inside my paybook a tag from Cicero,

recalled from school: '*Omnia mea porto mecum*' – 'All that I have I carry with me', but the boast wilted to nothing beside the inheritances of Indian poverty, which included malnutrition and all its associated diseases. Cholera never died in this city; it ruled in a fine state of health; Calcutta was its capital.

Before our train had crawled through miles of dispirited outskirts and dragged its length into Howrah Station, I was in a state of fascination. Nowhere, surely, could be more full of possibility, more free from the repressive judgements of home! That vibratory feeling never left me all the time I was in Calcutta. It was fantastic. Although I have spoken of it as a fortress of misery, its effect was stimulating. The brave Indians survived, flourished, in situations that would kill off Europeans.

They smile as they stand against a peeling wall, trying to sell miserable military badges, they wake in good heart after spending a night curled up in the rickshaw they pulled all the previous day. This is the capital also of man as a beast of burden – you need a licence to drag a rickshaw, and competition for one is formidable.

How can such a great machine work? Manpower alone is not the answer. Wherever man suffers, he sees to it that his womankind suffers at least as much. In the West, we have forgotten that over much of the globe women still exist in a state of slavery, to be traded and sold, to have their bones ground and sweet bodies exploited. Calcutta is also the capital of whoredom.

All this was true and more so in the Forties, for the structure of the city was forced to support, in addition to its natural burdens, an influx of warriors of all colours, British and American in particular. Many of those warriors might be permanently broke by the standards of their own country; by Calcutta's standards, they possessed enormous purchasing power. I was drawing the equivalent of twenty-five shillings a week; it made me a rajah in that great decrepit capital.

I knew what I wanted to buy.

Perhaps my desire was less to lie with a woman than to go in pursuit, to have a destination in that gigantic maze.

Our rear detail checked into a ghastly transit camp in Howrah and prepared, each in his own way, to get the most out of the evening. McGuffie was all set for a night's drinking and pontoon-playing, as were several of the others. He was setting up a school, together with a Scot from another unit, an uncouth man called Chambers with a large thistle tattooed on his chest.

I said to Tertis, 'Fancy a night out, Jackie?'

He shook his head. 'I'll sit in on the card-game and get an early kip.' He still would not look me straight in the face.

'You don't want to play with these hairy-kneed Scots or they'll have every last anna off you and leave you skint!'

'Och away to the brothels, man!' McGuffie roared. 'It's where ye were born and where ye'll dee!'

Calcutta was too big. I could not face it on my own. After a while, Feather agreed to join me. We spivved ourselves up, put on clean shirts, and strolled out of camp – by which time, our shirts were soaked with sweat. It was hot. My right leg and hand were hurting.

The sentry on the gate pointed us in the direction of town centre, and we headed hopefully along. Children were everywhere. In each of the blind arches under the railway bridge, whole families lived. Between permanent buildings, temporary shacks had been erected. Every house seemed to be bursting with people. The streets were full of beggars, wandering in the gutters or sitting with their backs against walls.

In such a dump, even shit had its value. Women collected animal droppings, made them into neat round pancakes, and slapped them against walls to dry. When the pancakes were baked dry, they fell to the ground. They were collected into frail baskets, the baskets were set on the women's heads, and the women went forth to sell. And most of these people had tranquil faces.

Even the shit-wallahs were doing good business. Everyone was busy flogging something. Poor though the place was, the system supported degrees of poverty in something like a buoyant state. We saw barbers shaving men in the street, squatting in the gutter to deliver a shave like a caress, in exchange for a cup of tea. And the *char*-wallah had a similar agreement with the butcher, who slept on his slab overnight.

Even poverty had its elegant gestures. Even the *char*-wallah had his almost naked young assistant. And when this child had handed over a cup of tea to barber or butcher, the latter would drink and then – with a flick of the wrist – cast his cup down to smash into the road. The cups were made of baked clay or mud, without handles. Perhaps there were Untouchables who picked a living out of mending the broken cups!

Everywhere, frantic trading was going on – to an outsider, most of it as incomprehensible as the languages spoken, each with its special intonation. As Feather and I got nearer the centre of the city, the pace hotted up. People were less dead, being richer. The crowds grew thicker. The buildings were slightly better, their iron balconies a shade less ramshackle, but all seemed more tightly crammed with humanity who had to stand out on the balconies because the rooms behind were so stuffed with heat and children – rather like endless chests-of-drawers so full of clothes that the drawers remain open and overflowing.

All this we saw in the special embalming kind of Indian darkness, lit by countless lamps and clattering trams, which crawled along under their sagging cables, belching green sparks at every intersection. The sparks were their way of protesting against the loads they had to carry – every vehicle bore white-clad youths draped from every possible vantage point outside.

This leech-like habit marked the entire commerce of the city. Anyone with anything to sell, from a bangle to a sister, could be relied on to follow potential customers for half-a-mile, arguing and pleading all the way. Many shops and most restaurants hired their own tenacious leech, chosen perhaps for a breath foul enough to drive you to take refuge in carpets or curry. These leeches were desperate. It was useless to pretend you did not want a carpet; he knew you did, and would hector you all the way up Chowringhee to prove it, throwing in desolating scraps of family history with each step of his argument.

Even among the beggars, competition was intense. The more cunning, not content with exposing whole battlefields of flesh given over to leprosy and syphilis (as we supposed the combatants to be), or amputated limbs, or scrotums inflated ten times life-size by elephantiasis, adopted a semi-official approach. They carried notebooks in which one was invited – implored – to enter one's name, together with the amount of donation. Here one could read of the extraordinary stinginess of world-famous figures who had contributed – sometimes frequently, never generously: Marie Lloyd, Charlie Chaplin, Adolf Hitler, Bing Crosby, Al Capone, Churchill, and Mickey Mouse.

Other beggars adopted a governmental approach, presenting their victims with a post card on which was written, in several curly languages, a brief history of their ill-luck, testified to by obscure officials.

Sir,

This unfortunate idiot is a lunatic from the malayli states. He has not escaped. He asks you to be excused. This is not his fault. The bearer was always dumb. He cannot speak since after birth. The foolish fellow and his brothers are also speechless and without voice. He lost his parent.

[179]

They early departed their sense. His younger sister is also blind and demented.

These three depend on this one. He laboured by the railway. Their mother was never known. His auntie died in the prime. His father was serving longwhile in South Indian Railway Co. Ltd, so Railway Officers have excused this imbecile and so kindly pay him charity and God help you.

Signed: A.R.M. Shoramanor Madras Dorosani Cristian.

Mrs. Pandambai, B.A. (Oxen) Principal

Theosophical Ladies' College, Lucknow.

Please to Re-Turn This Notice After The Execution

In this teeming world, nothing was what it seemed to be. The miseries of the idiot and his dependants were pissingly funny. The shit-*bibis* had the carriage and beauty of princesses. The humble tattooist on the street-corner, who would execute a red-and-blue cross entwined with thorns on your biceps for five chips, lifted a loin cloth to reveal a devil fucking a fat woman on his upper thigh. The chaps that robbed you in the bazaar had the world's most beautiful manners. The proud showed awesome humility. The humble could show an unassailable serenity. The religious mutilated themselves to demonstrate their wholeness. Calcutta was a welter of paradox.

Everyone seemed to possess a strict personal integrity. Even the most derelict or corrupt manifested it – yet they clearly hadn't a moral scruple among the whole variegated pack!

So I saw it then, for then it was less apparent to me that soldiers, like whores, have more business with rogues than with priests.

Whores were distributed all round the city. They stayed in their fetid little boxes while male pimps went out to comb the byways for customers; this was unlike the arrangement in the great whoring cities farther east – Singapore, Hong

Kong, and Macao, where you see what you are getting –
and, indeed, where what you are getting comes provocatively
to get you. The Indian whore keeps to her bed.

This kennelled mode of whoring lends her an indoor
aspect, an aspect of being inferior, of being merely market-
able goods, a hole with flesh round it priced not by the
pound but by the year, with maximum prices at about
sixteen; by twenty, they tend to drop. Not only do the prices
shrink, the rooms get smaller, the beds dirtier, and the
purchasing penises more inclined to shrivel at the sight of
monster cockroaches hurrying up the wall to break the
news to kith and kin.

All this Horatio Stubbs, aged twenty, young and hopeful,
gleaned from personal experience over the next few days –
that being the period he spent in the world's most dreadful
and inexhaustible city. To pack into those closed little
rooms with those open little whores – that was well enough!
But to hope (as I secretly did!) to find *love* there – that was
just madness!

I can hardly recall now what I expected to happen. I
suppose I hoped that the barrier of cash-for-flesh could be
broken, that one day I would confront a girl who was genuinely down on her luck, and that we would both recognize
in each other someone who was looking for a better life . . .
You believe many things, aged twenty.

Some girls told hard luck stories in their brittle little
collection of English words. I was never content merely to
fuck; I always wanted to hear from them as well. How
stereotyped their stories were! They all came from good
homes, most were daughters of maharajahs. One day when
they were very small, playing on the steps of the palace or the
big house, a bad man had come along (on horseback or
bicycle) and stolen them away. They had grown up in much
misery, locked away from human eyesight. And only
yesterday – or last week, or this very same evening, sir –

[181]

they had been sold to the terrible man who owned this brothel, and two picture-palaces as well.

Among the items in this much-told story, the picture-palace was rarely missing. All the whores, poor things, were cinema-goers. Which is not to suggest that their fantasies of kidnapping did not have some sound basis in the griefs of their real lives.

Some of the women immediately made their personality felt, even if they did not say a word. Sometimes I would be haunted by the expression with which one had regarded me, or by the quality of her embrace, or by some gesture that betrayed personal feeling. Then I would try to seek her out again. Often I could never find her – could never get back to the pokey street, could never identify the pokey building, or, having found street and building, could never find the girl again. She had gone: gone next door or a mile away: lost among the storm of dark and beautiful flesh that comprised Calcutta's entrails.

Terrible sensations of desolation would overawe me. A woman and a city! These sensations were hard to bear because I imagined that they would be laughed at by my fellows and because I was haunted by a feeling that I had undergone the same loss before. Yet it was not even a loss! – Just one more bit of cunt shuffling on her way! It was all irrational, and from the irrational there is no redress.

The first evening's brothel-going in Calcutta with Dave Feather was not a success. Mainly because we could not resist the tide of pimps, whose ranks thickened up considerably as we got to Chowringhee, the grand and over-taxed heart of Calcutta. It was impossible to walk ten yards without being offered someone's nearest and dearest.

We gave in to a villain with a limp and a turban, wasting

our money and semen in an offensive back-street, two floors up, where the whores were crowded five to a room. I was landed with a girl whose doss was actually out on a balcony, and had to bare my bum to the mosquitoes. While I worked away, her face would occasionally turn green, as a tram trundled by. We were virtually grinding on the street.

Feather and I got drunk after that. 'Here's to jungle warfare!', he said.

We arrived back in the Howrah transit camp at some unearthly hour, without a penny in our pockets, only to awaken everyone in the tent with our dreadful curses as we stumbled about. Finally, I flung myself under the mosquito net and fell into a sodden sleep.

I woke with a fearful headache. It took me a long while to stir myself. Only the pain of hearing eating irons clang against mess-tins, as chaps went to breakfast, forced me to move. I put some weight on my right arm. Pain immediately shot up my muscles and knobkerried my skull into a dozen distinct bits. I yelled with anguish.

'Get out of that fucking wanking-pit, ye drunken bugger!' McGuffie called cheerily. 'Soya-links for breakfast, just like Mither makes!'

I did get out, although my arm and hand never stopped hurting. My right leg was not too good either. I limped into the mess tent just in time to get the last cold ladleful of bergoo, and then could not eat it. For me, that was unheard of. After the meal, I had to lie on my *charpoy*. Everyone else was getting ready for parade. They came over and tried to persuade me to move. Eventually, aided by Carter the Farter and Aylmer, I rose and got my kit together.

Fortunately, parade was a farce, taken by a full corporal in the Pioneer Corps. We dismissed and I hobbled with my buddies to a nearby SSAFA canteen, where I soon began to feel a little better.

Carter and I put our names down for a game of football

that afternoon, not knowing whether we would still be there
to play. We had the word down from Gor-Blimey via
Dutt that some minor hitch had arisen, and that we would
be stuck in the camp for another night. So we had our game
of football.

By the time we got out on the field, my hangover had gone,
although I was still limping slightly. My hand hurt, but on
the wing I should have been able to keep it out of harm's
way.

It was dazzlingly hot – our squalid tents rippled in the
heat.

We had only been going about five minutes when the
inside right passed the ball out. I was off down the field with
the ball at my feet. The winger marking me was nowhere in
sight. As the back charged me, I flipped the ball back to the
inside right, who was where he should be – it was quite a
good forward movement for a scratch team. The back hit
me hard, crashing into my right side. Tremendous agony
ran through my wrist. The only relief came from walking
round in circles, which I did. Or I thought I did.

Faces clustered round me. They all seemed to be insisting
that I was helped off the field. Although I swore at them, it
did no good. They carted me off and in due course I found
myself being examined by a medical orderly.

'Are you all right, mate?'

'Let me get back on the field – that fucking sod of a back
fouled me.'

'What have you been up to? You've got a broken bone in
your hand.'

'It doesn't feel too good.'

'It's all swollen – look at it! There's a broken bone there
and you must get it seen to. You'll have to go into Number
Five Ambulance Unit on the racecourse. Get your kit
together!'

'What do I need my kit for?'

'They may have to keep you in for observation – overnight, like. Pack your night things in a small pack and get weaving, while I lay on transport.'

'Sod my fucking luck!'

'It's no good you fucking and blinding, mate. You'll just have to stop bashing the old bishop, won't you, now your right hand's out of action!'

So I found myself on the racecourse in the centre of Calcutta, where a medical unit had been set up. After I had checked in, I was examined by a captain in the Medical Corps, a bald man whose face bore a sceptical expression common to Army doctors. As I explained about my fall from the top of the train, his scepticism escalated until it wore deep grooves on either side of his nose.

'That may be, but you've broken a phalange or two, and probably a metacarpal. You may have torn a muscle as well.'

'So what do I do now?'

'You stop "falling off trains", for one thing.'

'Yes, but what do I *do*?'

The grooves bit a little deeper. 'You don't *do* anything, Private Stubbs! You have been done to. You are a casualty. We have an X-ray unit here, and you will be X-rayed in the morning. Your leg seems merely bruised.'

'I came down on some old rails and lumps of iron.'

'Very likely.'

I was established in a marquee tent which served as a ward. A few battered relics of the Forgotten Army lay about, exchanging long horror stories about Maungdaw and Razabil, or how their mules had sunk out of sight in the Arakan mud during the last monsoon. With their broken hairy shoulders, faded green vests, and identity discs dangling round their necks from dirty string, they did not even look like Mendips – in whom I always imagined I saw a family resemblance. These old sweats wanted to know how long I had been abroad, whether I'd ever heard a shot fired in anger, and whether I'd ever had to wear a french letter tied to my prick so that the leeches did not get up my pipe. When I disappointed them on all counts, they returned to a discussion of exactly how unreliable the Chinese were in battle.

I passed the time by feeling ill and feverish, and watching the bluebottles swarm up at the apex of the canvas above my head.

Delight filled me when, at about nine-thirty, a flow of angry lament reached my ears from outside. Jock McGuffie entered the tent and stood there surveying the scene. The Forgotten Army surveyed him. Instant hostility blossomed on both sides.

'What, are you fuckers all dying of something or other?' he asked the ward in general.

'Jock!' I called. 'Over here!'

'Christ, man, there's nae hope for ye, stuck in here wi' this lot!' McGuffie exclaimed, as he came across to my bed. 'They might as well bury the lot of ye and have done! Could they no' put a bit lighting in this pox-eaten dump? Yon sergeant on the gate's a right one, too, I'm telling you! Bloody big sandy-haired loon! He said to me, "You've no got a bottle of drink on ye, have ye?" Sassenach cunt! – What fucking business is it of his? "No, sarge," I says. "Now what would I be doing carrying around booze at this time of evening?" So he says to me, "There are some seriously sick men here. No drink's allowed in camp." No booze, I ask you! So I says, "If they're a bit down, surely it's a wee snort they need?" "These men have come straight out of Burma," he says. "Many of them's dying." "Ay, well, it does look a wee bit of a graveyard," I says.'

As he spoke, he pulled a bottle of beer from under his bush jacket and handed it to me. I thanked him and he opened it for me with the hook on the knife he always carried. We took it in turns to swig.

'I'm bloody glad to see you, Jock! I was afraid you lot
might move out and I'd be stuck in Calcutta on my own.'

'Those poor gits wouldn'e play pontoon tonight – just
because I fl ·ced them last night – so I thought I'd look you
up!'

He winked at me. 'We'll no be moving out yet awhile!' He
bent lower, looking furtive in the way he had done when
threatening to sort out old Spunk Bucket. He had been as
good as his word. Spunk Bucket was in the fertilizer right
up to his Adam's apple, even if he did not realize it yet.
McGuffie had fixed him good and proper.

'I told· you I'd got a mucker up at Division, didn't I?
Well, he was a good mucker – he helped me do the trick!
I've shafted old Spunk Bucket right up the *gonga*!'

His story emerged in the form of total recall. His mucker
at Division had slipped McGuffie a stencil kit and yellow
paint. When we were stuck in the railway siding at Indore,
Jock had got into one of the military bogies trucks full of
stores, while we were asleep and he was supposed to be on
guard. He had painted out the 2 Div flashes and identifica-
tions on the boxes and had readdressed them to 36 British
Division, then involved with the Japanese somewhere up in
the north of Burma. By now, these stores would be out of
Howrah station and heading for the great blue yonder!

'You're shitting me, Jock! You never did it!'

He passed me the bottle. 'I fucking did, Stubby, lad, just
like I say – what you take me for? And I took care to chuck
away the stencils afterwards. Spunk Bucket will fair be for it
now and no mistake!'

I took a swig of warm beer, stunned by the thought of
this sabotage.

'But why did you do it, Jock?'

He extracted the bottle from my grasp and took a leisurely
pull at the beer. 'Neither you nor I have any talent for
active service in Burma. It's a mug's game! As long as that

[187]

consignment of equipment is travelling round India, Burma, Assam, and China, rear detail's chances of staying put right here in Calcutta is good. The war in Burma's hotting up again and it's no place for gentlemen. Norm and me fixed this trick up before we left Kanchapur. Now, *you*'ve got to swear blind never to say a word about this bit of subversion to a soul, understand? There are plenty of dodgy bastards in this man's Army as would like to see old Jock McGuffie in the glasshouse for keeps!'

I swore blind.

'No' a word, mind! And now there's that bloody big sandy-haired sarge blowing off his mouth again!'

We could hear the sergeant shouting outside the tent. All visitors had to leave at once. Visiting time was over.

'I'd best be on my way!' Jock said, rising and draining the bottle of beer. 'You want to watch this lot here, too, I'm telling you, or they'll have that duff hand of yours cut off as soon as look at it, right up to the elbow. Here, I brought you another present – Jock looks after his mates!'

He fumbled in his capacious hip pocket and pulled out a crumpled paper-covered book, which I recognized as he tossed it to me. It was our prized copy of *The Night Times of Micheal Meatyard*.

'I made fucking sure that didn't get stencilled off to China!' Jock said.

It would be fair to say that McGuffie's news left me with mixed feelings. I had no wish to be in on his awful secret; he was surely guilty of sabotaging the war effort under the Defence of the Realm Act, or something equally unpleasant, while I was now an accessory who could be punished accordingly.

Whether or not his move would save us from the promised hells of Burma and Assam was another matter. For those hunting grounds I had developed something between fervent curiosity and the death wish; none of the Forgotten relics in the ward could alter that. Scared though I was by the thought of going into action, I had now begun to long for it.

All next day was spent hanging about between the ward, the X-ray unit, and the clinic, with a couple of visits to the orderly room thrown in for light relief. My hand and arm were growing more painful. Although my temperature was lower I felt too feeble even to read the exploits of Micheal Meatyard. In fact, I was off sex, and checked my tool once or twice, to see if it wasn't really the pox that had got me. At three in the afternoon, an orderly came round and told me to undress and get into bed. At five-thirty, I had a visitor. This time it was Captain Eric Gore-Blakeley.

I endeavoured to come to attention in the bed. Had he found out about the stencils?

'Sorry to hear about the broken bones, Stubbs. They tell me you have a temperature of a hundred-and-three. It's nothing in this heat, of course. Plenty of perfectly fit men are walking about with temperatures of a hundred-and-five. You've always been too fond of fighting.'

'Beg pardon, sir, this wasn't fighting. I fell off the roof of the train at Indore!'

He looked at me. 'That's what the M.O. told me you had told him. . . . Well, Stubbs, you've done yourself some damage. I've recommended you stay here for a few days and recover fully before you are discharged.'

Such solicitude! I knew there must be something behind it, and his next words confirmed my suspicions.

'As it happens, there has been a misunderstanding about some of our gear at Howrah station, so you are better out of the way.'

'Yes, sir.'

[189]

'Would you still be prepared to go on a wireless operator's course, Stubbs?'

'I suppose so, sir.'

'Good. I can't promise anything, of course, but there might be a course going locally.'

He was very neat in his officer's uniform, sweating slightly, and for once without his military air.

'And what about Burma, sir? Would the rest of the unit, the company and everything, go into action without us?'

'They might be forced to. You probably know that a Jap offensive is building up and, although their lines of communication are pretty much stretched, they still have plenty of punch behind them. If the offensive is coming, it will be at any time, since the monsoons are only two or three months away.'

'I'd rather join the company, sir, than be left behind.'

He did not answer that directly. 'General Slim, the Commander of the Fourteenth Army, is in the area now. The various units of 2 Div are also coming together. It could be that word to move will come through in a very few days – even a few hours.'

'What about our missing gear then, sir?'

He stood up. 'There's a war on. Perhaps the Army Command would forget the idea of an investigation.'

He paused as he turned to go. 'The rest of the rear detail is being transferred from the transit camp to a better camp nearby. We shan't lose touch with you, though. You won't get mislaid like the gear at Howrah!'

What did all that mean, I wondered, when he had left. Did he suspect me? Was he in fact planning to get rid of me in some way? Did he know Jock had visited me the previous evening? What was this fresh nonsense about a course?

All I could do was what one does most of in the Army: wait and see. But the waiting proved long and the visibility poor.

Next day, I was considerably better. The Forgotten Army jeered and spoke of malingerers who should get some service in when my temperature was pronounced to be down to normal. The sceptical medical captain informed me that I had cracked two bones and torn a flexor, whatever that was. My hand was bound up and my right arm put in a sling. I was excused fatigues and told to hang about camp.

The big sandy-haired sergeant of whom McGuffie had fallen foul proved to be perfectly friendly. He sought me out to give me advice. 'You don't want to listen too hard to Bedpan Bertie – he'd have every malaria case shipped home to the Blight! There's nothing to do here all day – you go into town and enjoy yourself. As long as you're back through the main gate by ten-thirty, nobody's going to worry what you're doing.'

'Thanks, sarge, but I've not got a rupee to my name.'

'We can't have that. Go to Corporal Harrison in the orderly room and tell him I sent you. He's a genius at causing money to circulate.'

Corporal Harrison was a chubby man with spectacles and fierce moustache. He polished the one and pulled the other, and produced fifteen rupees from a drawer, which sum he entered in my paybook. It was a week's pay.

Two days later, I was broke again – fifteen chips did not go far in Calcutta. The redoubtable Harrison paid me another week's pay.

'It's all right for him,' one of the Forgotten Army types said dolefully. 'He's got a load of dead 'uns on his payroll what peg out in this fucking camp and aren't never declared. You're living on dead man's wages, you are, mate.'

So I had a week exploring Calcutta on my own.

I tried to get in touch with my mates in the Mendips. To save money, I walked to the transit camp at Howrah. Our rear detail had upped and gone, leaving not a rack behind. Nobody knew anything about them, beyond the fact that they had moved in a fifteen-hundredweight Dodge truck early in the morning. A harassed lance-jack gave me a list of three other transit camps in the Calcutta area; but at this time troops were pouring in and out of the city, extra facilities were being set up, and in the confusion nobody seemed to know what was going on.

Another day, I walked to Sealdah railway station and found another transit camp. Nobody there had even heard of the Mendips.

At night, there was the irresistible temptation of the brothels – of being accosted, of giving in, of vanishing into the teeming stews, where cunt was as common as cockroaches. During the day, I wandered round the city, up to its gills in humanity, went round the gimcrack Jain temple, inspected the Rama Kristna Mart, watched the lorries, Sikh-driven taxis, and bullock-carts jostle each other over Howrah Bridge, looked at the docks, and had myself ferried down the Hooghly to the Botanical Gardens, where I sat under the biggest banyan tree in the world, propped up on its multitude of stilts like a too-successful beggar.

It was amazing to be alone again, away from other people. By the end of the week, with my arm out of the sling, I did a little sketching, half bashful at this display of artistic temperament.

When I got back to the camp one lunchtime – despite Harrison's payments, I was almost broke again – the big sandy-haired sergeant called me over.

'There's a message come over the blower for you soon as you'd cleared off this morning.'

'From "A" Company?' I was leaning in the doorway.

'Very likely. A *gharri*'s coming to pick you up here at sixteen hundred hours, and you've to report to 26 Reinforcement Camp.'

'Where's that, sarge?'

'I hate to tell you this, lad, but it's at Dimapur. You're going to have a chance to stop the Japs marching on India. It's action for you at last.'

It was stuffy in his little wooden office, almost as hot as outside. Among all the duty rosters and lists of units, there were pin-ups from '*SEAC*' hanging on the wall.

In a moment of revelation, I wondered what the fuck I had been doing with my life. A glimpse came to me of myself as a kid, clinging on to my big brother Nelson in terror, while he fended off a furiously barking dog. Nelson was in action near Monte Cassino – for all I knew he was dead now! I'd never really had the chance to be myself, whoever that was, had I? These last bloody years had been occupied with pretending to be a Mendip – and this is where it had got me.

Am I capable of understanding my own life? I write it all down, and it comes back like someone else's life. At that instant, half-inside the hot little office, with the sandy-haired sergeant watching me, I knew . . . no, I've forgotten what I knew then.

The month of March, 1944, was almost spent. The flow of events, of time itself, was heavier in the South-East Asian theatre of war than in Europe. In Europe, the Nazis were being smitten on every front, and victory seemed assured. In India, we had hardly made a start against the Japs, and the territory to be recovered was appalling in extent. The American general, 'Vinegar Joe', was battling away with his Chinese troops in the north of Burma, and British troops had managed local gains in the Arakan. But the Japs still enjoyed their dreadful reputation for being merciless as conquerors and impossible to defeat. Now they were moving west towards the gates of India, marching out of the plains of Central Burma – as even I knew from my reading of the newspaper.

So much for whatever plans McGuffie or Gor-Blimey might have. So much for me. Nodding to the sergeant, I went off to the marquee, a little pale about the gills. Dimapur was the capital of Dimapur State, next to Assam, on the very brink of Burma, and a long way forward from the randy glitter of Calcutta.

The dregs of the Fourteenth Army sensed there was something up, and soon got my news out of me. Shrieks of delight greeted it.

'You lucky fucker! Now's your bloody chance to get some service in! About time you bloody base-wallahs did your share! You'll be marching the Dimapur Road in no time!'

One of the chief shits was a bent-nosed REME man called Cuxham. He was round-shouldered and talked indistinctly, spitting over his '*s*'es, as if he had an exceptionally tacky lower lip on which his protruding teeth were liable to stick. He strolled over as I was collecting my gear and said, 'Ffo, you're going to be a Chindit, iff that it?'

'I just hope I'm going to rejoin my mates, that's all I know.'

'You'll be lucky!'

'What a fucking way to run an army!'

'It'f no good, mate, they've diffcovered you're malingering – you're for it, you'll never ffee your matef again! You're jufft fucking Jap fodder, you are!'

I hit him smack in the mush. Not very hard but pleasureably hard. My right fist did not hurt a great deal – not as much as his face hurt him. Cuxham lurched away and went down the far end of the ward to sit on his *charpoy* and clutch

his head. His mates all gathered round him, pressing Wog
Players on him. One of them looked sickly over at me and
called, 'You're a cruel young bleeder, you are! Poor old
Cuxy was caught by the Yellow-bellies in the Admin Box
at Ngakyedauk – he didn't mean no harm.'

'No? Then why didn't he leave me a-fucking-lone? He's
bloody *puggle*, that's his trouble.' All the same, I felt more
ashamed than I showed, as I always did when I lashed out.

One of the other chaps said in a melancholy way, 'We're
all going fucking *puggle* in this bastard climate. If you ask me,
before we get out of here, the whole *submukkin* pack of us'll
be *puggle*!'

'I didn't mean to hurt him. Why didn't he hit me back?'

'You wouldn't fucking ask that if you'd been at fucking
Ngakyedauk, having to eat the mules and listening to the
Japs *boloing* your name after dark. How can you know what
it's like if you've been no further fucking east than Firpo's?'

'I'm going to find out now, aren't I?'

One of Cuxham's muckers said sullenly, 'It'll be cushy
from now on, what with fucking air-drops and everything.
You can't call it war any more.'

It did not take me long to get my few belongings together.
I slung my pack over one shoulder and made for the entrance.
There was a lance-corporal in the tent whom they called
Lackeri, a clerk – I knew he had been caught in the Ngakye-
dauk admin box because I'd heard him gripping about it. He
stopped me at the entrance. An old man of thirty, wearing
Army specs, his identity discs swinging against his hollow
chest, a sweat-rag tied round his neck.

'Good luck, old boy! All the best! You'll come through it
okay. Pay no heed to this lot of *admis* – they've had it.
Things are better than what they was in our time! Take it
easy!'

I stared at him. We just looked at each other. People were
always leaving places in those days and moving on.

'I didn't mean to sock your mate – I was sweating on the top line.'

'Don't you take no notice of these bods. They've been out in the sun too long. They're due for repat. Take care of yourself, old lad!' He clapped me on the shoulder, nodding his head once.

I hurried over to the bogs. Shutting myself in one of the cubicles, I burst into tears. There seemed to be no way to stop. I just sat there and cried; I couldn't take being spoken to kindly like that.

After a bit, I pulled myself together and lit a fag. I was safe there. The other sounds of the shithouse – slamming doors, farts, pee escaping – came from far away, as I tried to survey my life. Burma. It was just that it was so final . . . it would be exciting. But not to get another screw in! My hand was okay again. Maybe I could go and see the M.O., that sceptical bloke, and pretend that one of the bones . . . no, fuck that for a lark! But no screwing. . . . When would I ever have a lovely long messy slobbering sexy love affair with a girl? A white girl; England. Or a Chinese girl, one of those beauties I'd seen in Chowringhee the other day, smashing faces, marvellous legs. God, Christ, what a twot I was not to have had a Chinese girl yesterday – today was too late. No dough. The Chinese girls were more expensive than the *bibis*. You could see why. Can you just imagine their sweet little tits and glorious little cunts. . . .

Well, one could always dream, and wank at the same time. By sprawling right back on the seat and ignoring the stink of the shit-pit below me, I managed in no time to lob some spurts of spunk over my stomach, with some relief. It was not wholly a milestone as wanks go because the smoke from my fag got into my eye.

As I was getting up and industriously faking the sound of arse-wiping with the newspaper provided, I heard someone come into the shitter for a pee, I heard their snatch of song.

Could I but see thee stand before me. . . .

It was sixteen hundred hours. The *gharri* had come to collect me, with at least one of my friends. Thank God, I'd be off to Burma with someone I knew!

book 3
God's Own Country

God's own country was the ironical Fourteenth Army name for Burma. Perhaps it was so named because of the difficulty of getting there. The distance from Calcutta to Kohima in Assam – maintaining the celestial topography, Assam was God's Frontier Post – had to be measured in more than miles. The rear detail of the First Battalion travelled northwards by train, on a railway taken over and run by US Railway Troops. From the train, we transferred to a ferry, and the ferry took us slowly across the wide Bramaputra. On that river's eastern shores, we stood in Assam and the effects of the Japanese blight were already apparent. The chaos and splendour of India, the cheerful and hazardous trafficking of its people, all shrank away into the unnatural quiet of an invasion area. Such inhabitants as there were moved the way people do in war-zones – keeping close to the fence. We were far from home.

We climbed on to another train – this time of a narrower gauge than the first, as if the sinister Japanese spell had caused even the railway to contract with fear. This train started with more than Indian promptness and brought us to Dimapur.

Every change of transport meant delays. It also meant the unloading of stores – McGuffie might have lost a military bogie full of our stores, but there were plenty of other stores to be humped. This chain of supply, over different gauges, rivers, and mountains, was the only route to the central front in Burma, bar the air!

The country grew more tremendous as we advanced, as if it too was heading for some kind of crisis. Each change of transport entailed spending a night in a transit camp; each morning, we woke to chill air and, although the sun quickly became as blazingly hot as ever, we knew we were heading towards higher mountains. I don't know how it was with the others, but for me those were days of excitement. I could have travelled on for ever.

On this journey, the foreign names stood out like names of an incantation: in particular, Dimapur, Kohima, and Imphal! Imphal, the most distant, was capital of the tiny state of Manipur – a capital yet a village – Kohima was just a village in the Naga Hills of Assam, some fifty miles beyond Dimapur. In the ranks, we made little distinction between Manipur and Assam and Burma – all tropical trouble-centres.

As we rolled into Dimapur, everyone stood at the windows of the train staring out in amazement.

'Hey, I reckon the fucking Japs have taken over here already!', Tertis said.

The pitiful little town was packed with soldiery and refugees and thousands of coolies. This was the bottle-neck between India and Burma and, for every man going forward, eastwards, there were ten trying to get back, westward. As the valley opened out, the panorama resembled an historical frieze more than reality. Dust roads stretched in all directions. Along them roared camouflaged lorries, one behind the other almost bumper to bumper, travelling at reckless speeds. There were long static lines of coolies, too, often engulfed in dust. In the valley and on the hillside, impromptu camps were being flung up. Digging was going on everywhere. The whole impression this great staging area gave was of chaos.

An invasion had taken place, as Jackie Tertis implied.

In the centre of town stood a signpost with three fingers, each pointing in a different direction and reading, 'NEW YORK 11,000 miles, TOKYO 5,300 miles, LONDON 8,300 miles'. As the pecking order of cities indicated, Americans were in town. As usual, the American troops looked more relaxed, more democratic, bigger, and decidedly better fed than our troops; they differed as much from us in those respects as we did from the Indian sepoys.

The mixture of races was staggering. It was as if all these thousands of strange men had suddenly arrived to build a new Tower of Babel in this unknown spot. We saw Chinese troops, who were reserved, and Gurkhas, who waved cheerily ('Yon's the best fucking fighting man in the world, after your Glaswegian,' McGuffie said), and a contingent of West Africans – not to mention a baffling miscellany of Indian and Assamese troops. Everyone was on the move.

For all the over-crowding, our little party moved into a neat and almost empty staging camp. It had been set up for 2 Div. We were almost the first of the division to arrive at the scene of action. The rest were straggling, train-load by train-load, across India, towards this narrow and dangerous valley which pointed towards Kohima and the advancing Japanese.

Our party grabbed some food and then went to see a film show: Tom Conway in 'The Falcon in Danger'. The film was projected on to canvas, so that the audience could sit on the ground on both sides of the screen. Who cared on which side of his head Conway parted his hair?

Chatting with other squaddies, we gained a basic picture of what was happening in the so-called real world about us. Japanese units were moving forward again, threatening Kohima and encroaching on the Dimapur-Kohima and Kohima-Imphal roads. Nobody knew precisely where they were. The Dimapur-Kohima road was overlooked by mountains, every mountain covered by jungle right up to its crest; some of the chaps had seen Japs moving about on the crests. 33 Corps was supposed to be guarding this vital length of road – 'and they're a bloody shower,' someone lugubriously remarked.

'The Mendips'll sort them fucking Japs out!' Carter the Farter said. He laughed.

We walked down the valley road, smoking and chatting, to a canteen in a tent where they were serving chicken buttis and beer. Over the Naga Hills, a half-moon sailed. London 8,300 miles. In the tent, a group of Cockneys were arguing drunkenly about the exact route a Number 15 bus took.

I stood outside drinking my pint and smoking. I didn't want to talk to anyone. All the expectations of yesterday had been swept away. It was enough to stand in this magnificent valley.

My mates had told me their news: how they had been transferred to Barrackpore as soon as I had left for the Field Ambulance Unit, how Gore-Blakeley had been going spare about the missing equipment, and how everything had suddenly become irrelevant because the Japs were on the move and every able-bodied man in India was being pushed up to meet them. Whatever schemes McGuffie or Gore-Blakeley or anyone else had nourished – all were blown away. The lists had arrived, the orders went through, we did as we were told.

There was a remote outburst of firing, echoing down among the hills.

'Probably Jap mortars – they're bastards with their mortar-fire,' Ernie said.

'Some poor bastard's getting it,' Aylmer said. He and I walked back to our *basha*, leaving the others. It was the first firing – the first real firing – we had heard. Here and there, groups of men were singing in the darkness. Convoys were moving in both directions. Sepoys were on guard all along

the road, at the stage of night with friends to keep them
company smoking *beadis*, the pungent scents of which
followed us down the road.

'At least we should be going in with Yankee Lee-Grant
tanks,' Aylmer said reflectively. 'The old Valentines they
used in the Arakan were no use – should have been *pegdoed*
long ago – obsolete. They've been handed over to the
Chinese now, so I hear.

I laughed. 'They'll do for the fucking Chinese!'

'The Chinese are fine fighting men. The old Yanks won't
have a scrap without electric-razor sockets in their landing
craft, but your Chink is brought up to fight on a handful of
rice a day. A Chink'll go for days on just a handful of
rice. They're like the Japs, given the chance. I wouldn't mind
if they were going in with us.'

It was the second time he had used that expression 'going
in'. He seemed to savour it.

'Christ, it's a fucking lovely night!', I said.

We heard firing again, followed by the plummy sound of
mortars.

Next day was a waiting day for rear detail. Most of them
were pressed into digging slit-trenches; McGuffie and I went
off with Captain Gore-Blakeley, Jock driving his Jeep, I
lugging my wireless set and passing an occasional message to
or from White Knight, which was someone at Corps HQ.
Gore-Blakeley had with him a Major Bedford, a Division
Officer, in charge of supply dispersal or something. They
seemed to enjoy themselves, driving about everywhere,
walking miles. Jock was often able to sit tight in the Jeep
while I tagged after them on foot, sweating beneath the set-
harness, half-listening to their conversation.

They were both very cool and detached about the

prospects for the battle, as though discussing the chances for a season's football fixtures. Bedford was the senior prefect.

'The sooner 8 Brigade moves in the better,' he said. 'We've got a very mixed bag defending Kohima, although they hold good defensive positions. The Japs are much thicker on the ground than we realized at first. Mutaguchi and Sato are first-class commanders and, if they over-run Kohima, Dimapur would be impossible to defend. I needn't stress how disastrous it would be for India and the UK if they took Dimapur.'

'Supposing they by-pass Kohima, as they have Imphal?'

'We shall have to do the best we can.'

'Naturally.' Perhaps Gor-Blimey felt at a disadvantage. He said quickly, '2 Div is moving into its concentration areas as fast as possible. As you know, units have to assemble from as far afield as Chittagong and Ahmednagar.'

'It's that damned line of communication back to India! Fortunately, the Japs' lines are even more extended.'

'The monsoons will make everything impossible. I hate to think of the water that pours off these hillsides in the wet season.'

Bedford had a way of wiping his moustache with an open hand as if it kept filling with sweat and needed to be frequently squeezed dry. He wiped it now with some perseverence. 'We're learning to fight over any terrain, under any conditions.'

'Agreed entirely. But it would clearly be better if we could drive Sato back into the central Burmese plains before the wet season. The British soldier is more accustomed to fighting in open country.'

Lowering his voice in the hope that I, trudging along in the rear, would not hear, Bedford said, 'Most of the units in this area are unaccustomed to *any* mode of fighting – with notable exceptions, they've never fired a rifle in anger in their lives.'

'8 Brigade are as highly trained as any unit in this theatre of war.'

'Thank God for that but – without wishing to cast a damper in any way – your chaps have been trained in combined ops. They may find the mountain jungles ahead a different kettle of fish entirely.'

'You should be pleasantly surprised within the next few days.'

'Of course I expect to be. It's a matter of first urgency to get the brigade up the road to its concentration area at Zubza, and out of this bloody shambles.'

Bedford indicated the muddle of rifle pits and barbed wire through which we were walking. Hundreds of spare bods stood about or sat on piles of kit. Coolies wandered aimlessly everywhere. You could go a long way – we did go a long way – before seeing anyone with a rifle. Only in the reinforcement camps was there order and a military scheme of things. We toured the defences in an alternating state of anger and expectation, eventually arriving at an air-strip, where Bedford and Gore-Blakeley disappeared into an officers' mess and Jock and I scrounged a fried egg, a couple of bully sandwiches, a can of plums, and *char* from an aircraftsman's cookhouse. This feast we ate on the edge of the airstrip, watching the planes – mainly RAF Vengeances – land or take off in the dust and daylight.

'If we could think of a way of getting on to one of they wee planes, we could be back in Calcutta and pissed before fucking sunset,' Jock said wistfully. 'I'll maybe go and chat up some of them pilots. Bet you there's a Glasgey lad there somewhere! Come on!'

'I'll stay by the Jeep. Have a bash, Jock!'

'Okay, you unsociable bugger – just don't flog the vehicle to anybody.'

He nodded and marched off, with that parody of a march he reserved for his public performances. I noted that for once he was making a tactical error. The parade-ground stomp was out in Dimapur, where it raised too much dust; the fashion was for a sort of brisk stroll, a gun-fighter's walk.

The guns were hammering away in the hills when my two officers reappeared.

'Sounds as if we're bashing the Japs again, sir,' I said to Gor-Blimey.

'Do you fancy a bash at them yourself, Private Stubbs?' Bedford asked. Testing morale, no doubt.

I nodded my head and smiled in idiot Tommy Atkins fashion. 'Me, sir? Signaller Stubbs, sir. Not 'arf, sir!'

He smiled back, attempting once more to wipe the moustache off his face. 'Well, the sooner you get your chance the better. If the Japs get this far, India could be theirs. It's a pretty rugged prospect. You should be moving up to engage before very long.'

'We'll give 'em what for, sir!'

'I'm sure you will.'

Three Hurribombers went snarling past overhead, speeding up the valley towards Kohima.

To Bedford, Gor-Blimey said, 'Someone's going to "give 'em what for", by the looks of things.'

'Just as well. We've got precious little strike-power on the ground in Kohima at present – the Assam Regiment, almost untried, plus the Assam Rifles, who are just local police, a few odds and sods of the Burma Regiment, and our friends and allies of the Nepalese Army! Hardly the most solid defence against a crack Japanese division like the 31st.'

'A hybrid mixture.' The officers lit cigarettes. Gor-Blimey leaned against the Jeep and looked up at the hills with the nonchalant eye of a grouse-shooter.

'Damned hybrid mixture!' Bedford said. 'That's part of the charm of the Fourteenth Army. A signals captain at Ranking's last committee meeting was likening us to the armies of Austria-Hungary at the beginning of the Great War. I shut him up! I thought the parallel was one that hardly needed stressing.'

'Hardly! The British have always used native contingents – because of our small population, I suppose. I hear the Japanese are using Koreans.' He turned abruptly to me. 'We should be moving. Stubbs, where is McGuffie?'

'He's just nipped off to the latrines, sir. Here he comes now!'

We watched McGuffie swinging his arms as he marched across the dusty plain towards us, looking every inch an un-sung hero.

'Just went to collect some fags, sir!' he said, saluting smartly.

We were called at five next morning, before dawn had broken. The world was silent and fantasmal, embalmed in a chill air. It felt like the middle of the night. We had a cold wash, dressed, packed up our things, and lugged them over to the mess, where surly cooks were dishing out the first bergoo of the day. Other soldiers were there at the mess tables, a despatch rider in leather coat all covered in dust, three Aussies who did not speak, various wild-looking characters. Jam stood on the trestle tables in great cans. As always, I was ravenous.

'Where we going, Corp?'

'Join the rest of "A" Company, of course.'

We moved over to a dispersal point and were checked out, and Corporal Dutt marched us to a supply dump, where an RASC Corporal set us to loading rations into a five-tonner. It was just getting light.

Beginning to feel more like a fighting troop, I asked the corporal-in-charge why we were set to loading rations.

'You lot got to get up that road, *thik-hai*? These rations is due for Kohima, *malum*? You're lucky to be travelling up with 'em, in comfort. If I had my way, you lot would march up the bloody road, and then we'd have more room in the transport for rations, but the road's choked up enough already without you terrible hairy 8 Brigade *wallahs* stragglin' over it.'

'Pity they didn't build a wider road then,' I suggested.

He stood stock still and glared at me. 'What ignorance!' His contempt almost overwhelmed him. 'You're a base-*wallah*, mate, aren't you? Just come in from Firpo's with the ice cream still wet round your bloody mouth! You want to take a fucking good *shufti* at that road as you goes over it this morning, and remember when you do that every inch of the way was built on human sacrifice, just as in days of old!'

There was reason to recall what he said, and he was with us to remind us. When the lorry was loaded, we piled in, and it moved to form up on a feed road with the next convoy to go through. Day was fully on us now. We could see the scar of the road, yellow and brown, against the mountainside – and then realized that that was only another feed: the proper road lay high above it, in the low clouds.

What a drive that was, once we got started! We had Indian drivers who, despite the odds placed against their doing so, kept us on the road. It must have been a challenge to any man. The marvellous road curled continuously round the mountainsides with the dexterity of a contour-line on a map. It rarely ran straight for more than a few yards.

The RASC corporal gave us a commentary, pointing excitedly as the early morning sunshine swung first in the back then in the front of our *gharri*.

'Watch this bit now! A *gharri* went over the *khud* here a couple of days ago and started a minor avalanche. They're still patching up the damage.'

Gangs of native workmen, muffled in old sweaters or

tunics, worked with baskets by the road where he indicated and there were others just over the edge of the bank, clinging to what looked like a sheer drop.

'They're the blokes as built this magnificent engineering enterprise – gangs of Indians and Assamese and Nagas and the bleeding lot, what you wouldn't look twice at normally – built it all on their tod, with a bit of help from our sappers and suchlike. Don't it make you weep to see it? Now you know why the British Empire's great!'

'You mean we exploit all the good road-builders!' Carter the Farter said.

'I'll throw you over the *khud*, mate, if you talk like that! Look out there! Just take a *shufti*! What ennerprise! I come up here most days and never get sick of the sight!'

Sitting on the piles of bully-cans, we stared out with him. It certainly was a marvellous road. Down in the valley, several hundred feet below, we saw an occasional burnt-out lorry, where an unlucky driver had not been quick enough with brake or wheel. The scenery was wild and magnificent. All of us, from time to time, glanced furtively up at the crests of hills, looking for Japs.

Some way beyond the Nichugard Pass, we had a long halt for more than an hour. An advance Jap patrol several miles ahead, had blown a bridge during the night. We waited without complaint until traffic could move again, standing on the road with the sun scorching our arms and foreheads. Lorries could be seen far ahead, moving round their shoulders of the road, long before it was our turn to jump aboard and go ahead.

The sense that the die was cast was strong on us. Calcutta had sunk far below the plimsol line. We could only guess at what lay ahead. Even McGuffie was silent this morning, beyond an occasional curse at the driver to take the curves easy. His attempt to sneak an air-lift back to Calcutta the day before had come to nothing – the pilots had all been

Canadian – and he was content to listen to the oratory of the RASC corporal.

We arrived at Milestone 35, where Battalion HQ was still being established. A crude roadside sign pointed up a side track to our concentration area.

'All change!' yelled the RASC corporal. 'This is Zubza. No cinemas or cushy air-conditioned restaurants here!'

Without wasting time, we threw our kit down on to the dusty verge. The corporal stared at me as I climbed over the tail-board.

'Well, Firpo, p'raps you learnt sommink this morning!'

'It's quite a road, I give you that.'

'Quite a road! Sod me! I'll say it is! It's the Eighth Wonder of the World, after Stonehenge and Edison's Lighthouse!' He banged his open palm against the side of the truck as a signal to the driver. '*Jhaldi jao*! Kohima!'

He gave us a thumbs-up sign as the lorry disappeared in the swashbuckling dust.

The heat of day was intense as we reported in and moved uphill to our new positions.

'Here comes the old monkey god himself!' There was Wally, with the rest of our mates, whom we had not seen since Kanchapur. He came up and smote me affectionately on my biceps. 'How's Vishnu and the rest of your fucking pin-ups then, Stubby?'

'In my big pack, you old sod, along with *Micheal Meatyard*. How're you doing, cobber?'

Wally, Dusty Miller, Di Jones, Enoch, and the others looked wilder than they had done in Kanchapur, tougher, and browner. We stood about for a while, joking and laughing, until RSM Payne came and moved us on.

'It's great here, cocker,' Wally said, walking along with me. 'Not like fucking Kanchapur or Vadikhasundi. We've only been here a couple of days – had a scare just as we were digging in. The picket exchanged a few rounds with a party of wandering Japs. The hills are lousy with 'em.'

'Bet you shit yourself, Page!' Carter laughed. 'Churchill won't help you here, you fucking old Tory!'

'I don't see Joe Stalin tagging along with you neither,' Wally said, good-humouredly.

'How's Geordie Wilkinson?' I asked.

Wally lifted his bush hat and mopped his forehead. 'He needs his mum!'

The novelty of being half-way up a mountain was infectious. We were jumpy and excited. When Charley Meadows came along to show Carter the Farter and me where to dig our slit trench, he clearly shared the general excitement. Only Geordie, when he showed up, seemed less enthusiastic.

'You won't find any knocking-shops up here, like, mate, I'm afraid. No football, either.'

'Seen any Japs yet, Geordie?'

Geordie's Adam's apple started to bob. He made obscure gestures to me, trying to get me to one side so that Carter, a well-known mocker, did not hear what he had to say. I moved over to oblige him.

'We only got here like a couple of days ago – at least it seems longer, but that's all it is, just a couple of days. And the Japs opened fire on us as soon as we got here.'

'I heard the picket had loosed off a few rounds at someone.'

'Look, mate . . .' He grabbed my arm. 'The fucking bullets, I mean. I swear they were aiming at me – well, not aimed *at* me, like, but I was *on* that fucking picket, and Christ . . . Honest, mate, I nearly got wiped out, like, as soon as I got here. I mean, perhaps I'm unlucky or something. A sort of Jonas, you know what I mean? The bloke that got swallowed up by the what's-it, the whale . . .'

'For Christ sake, Geordie, fuck off, man! We're all going to get fired at, aren't we? That's what we're here for, isn't it?!'

He went sulky. 'It's all right for you, mate, you don't care.
You're as bad as Wally, you never fucking care, but some
bloke in the factory *told* me I was a Jonas once.'

'You mean a Jesus. A Weeping Jesus!'

'How about lending a hand with this bastarding trench,
Stubbs?' Carter the Farter called. 'It's like hacking your way
through fucking millstones.'

'Get on with it, Carter! Stop moaning! I thought you
were a Communist and believed in working for the general
good!' I turned to Geordie. 'Pull yourself together, Geordie,
for Christ's sake! You're okay. The Japs missed you, didn't
they?'

'You can say that . . . It's cushy for you – I suppose that
Monkey God thing brings you luck, like, or summat . . . You
were down in Chowringhee with Carter and fucking
McGuffie when they were firing at me. You know that
McGuffie's a real bastard, don't you? I bet you were having
a poke down there in Cal, weren't you?'

'You were there yourself. Didn't you have a poke? I bet
old Wally did!'

'Oh, yes, old Wally did . . .'

'Right – well, you'd be feeling a fucking lot better now if
you'd had a poke right alongside him.'

'There's no survival value in fucking . . .'

'Oh, Jesus, fuck *off*, Geordie, will you, do you mind!'

'That's all you care, like! Fine mucker you turned out to
be!' He moved off and I went to help Carter. Some of our
natural excitement had begun to wear off by the time Carter
the Farter and I had dug ourselves a slit-trench. The ground
was tough and stony and needed a lot of work. We pitched
our two-man bivouac over it and breathed deep, while
sweat poured off us.

'This is a right way to start our holidays in Assam,' I said.

Carter patted the tent affectionately. 'What the hell, it's
home!' We began to sing together:

[211]

It's only a shanty in old shanty town . . .

We were still singing when Sergeant Chota Morris, my old buddy in No. 1 Platoon, came up the trail. He too looked wilder and browner than in Kanchapur.

'How does it feel to know that there are twenty thousand murdering little sods of Japs out there, creeping towards you, Horry?'

'Christ, they don't know I'm here yet, do they?'

' 'Course they do, boy – the news is back in Tokyo by now!'

'When do we actually have a go at them?'

'No good asking me. Nobody seems to know exactly where the Japs are, or how many divisions they've got in the area. They're attacking Imphal in strength – that's sixty-five road miles south of Kohima, but they may have a couple more divisions between here and Imphal.'

'And how far's Kohima from here? Only about ten miles, isn't it?'

'That's not the point. We've got to hang on till the whole Div gets here, and then we can't just move up the road, not just like that.'

'Why the fuck not?'

'Because it would be too easy for this bloody army!' Carter interposed.

Chota said, 'Anything moving along that road is liable to be picked off from the hills. It's a perfect target! You can't hold the road without holding the hills, can you? So my bet is that we'll soon get cracking into these ridges behind us – and we won't get cracking until all the gash bods in the area are sent back to base.'

We stood contemplating the savage planes of jungle all round us.

'Makes a change from Kanchapur!'

'We'll knock the shit out of the Japs. It's going to come out in bucketsful. They've had their own way out here too long.

Once we stop them here, we can bowl them back into Burma
and out the other side.'

He made it sound like a village cricket match played with
turds for balls.

'Why should we bloody bother about what happens to
Burma?' Carter the Farter asked. 'I'd never heard of the
bloody dump till I come out to India.'

'It's not Burma so much, we've got to hold on to India,
haven't we?'

'Why?'

'Don't be fucking daft, man, because it's ours, isn't it?'

'Carter's a Communist,' I said. 'You don't want to take
any notice of what he says! He thinks the king and queen
should move out of Buckingham Palace and live in a council
flat.'

Chota Morris laughed. 'I suppose you think we're
oppressing the Indians, do you? They'd be a fucking sight
worse off without us looking after them.'

Carter always rose to such bait. 'Balls! Arseholes! The
British ruling classes are oppressing the Indians just as they
oppress the British working man. If we stood back and let the
Japs have India, we'd all be freer.'

'You'd be working on the fucking Death Railway for one!'

'Besides, what about the rights of the Japanese working
man?' I asked.

'I'll shoot the bastard when I see him,' Carter said, and
we all burst out laughing.

I stood under a low tree to cool off and look about at the
superb landscape through which the Japanese working man
might even now be crawling. A leaf fell off a twig and
spiralled down to the ground. It lay there in the sun, green
at my feet. I had a fag. My mind wandered. I just felt fucking
lucky to be there, to be among my mates again, to be standing in the middle of that marvellous country. I was fitter and
tougher than I had ever been, wanking twice a day without

noticing it, burning off surplus energy. The air was like armour – it blazed and it had advanced from the Himalayas, not so far away. You could suck it down your throat like beer.

In twenty minutes, the leaf by my boots had turned brown. In half-an-hour, it was shrivelled and dead, lost, forgotten among the debris underfoot.

That night, the garrison at Kohima was heavily attacked; the concentration of Japs in the area was growing. Two nights later, the siege was on in earnest. We lay awake in our slit-trenches, listening to the firing.

The tremendous task of moving in our division, with all its guns and equipment, through that crazy line of supply from India, went on. Behind our defences above Zubza, we passed our days as picturesquely as outlaws. Our hand-kerchiefs and sweat-rags and any white articles of clothing we possessed were dyed jungle-green in a vat made from an oil drum, cut in two and placed over an open fire. We were issued with an amazing new American chemical called DDT, which we rubbed along the seams of our clothes to keep bugs out, since we were unlikely to be washing clothes for a while. We ate mepacrine and vitamin tablets. We cleaned rifles, and I was issued with a sten gun instead of a rifle. I worked the wireless set, and found how baffling it was to establish communication by short wave in a mountainous area.

We were also addressed by the C.O. of the Battalion, Willie Swinton. He told us that we were about to fight and win one of the great victories of the war, that our fame was assured, and that never again would we be called the Forgotten Army.

'While we're winning victories, we aren't doing anything worse,' Bamber said, parodying himself.

We patrolled. We picketed. We watched. We waited. It was all rather exciting. We were playing soldiers.

Only a few days before, I had been in Calcutta, surrounded by all sorts of petty worries. They had gone, they were obsolete. We were in action now. We had nothing, or nothing that we couldn't carry with us. We were hunters.

I felt myself stripped to the bone. For once, I understood everything that was going on around me, because everything had been reduced to its most primitive. We had to crawl round our allotted hillsides, keeping in touch with neighbouring units, watching for the enemy. Although I had never considered myself cut out for that sort of thing, ancient instincts woke and growled in pleasure.

That Assamese landscape had a lot to do with it. How back-breakingly tremendous it was! Sometimes we had to move up to the top of a ridge, two thousand feet above the road and another thousand above the valley. Clouds drifted below us. We scrambled over burning rock or moved in single file up sandy *chaungs*, which would be raging streams when the monsoons came. But the monsoons were weeks away yet. Perfect summer reigned and the pure air could burn by day and freeze by night with hardly a dusty bush stirring in its sleep.

The mountainside was covered with trails. The first time that we were near enough to any Japs to shoot them, we had to hold our fire. A column of them passed, and we were only a section patrol. They were moving along one of the trails, only a few yards above us. When they had gone, Charley Meadows passed the word back over my set to HQ, reporting strength and direction of the column.

As I crouched over the wireless, I looked round at the faces of my mates. A memory returned of how I had at first priggishly thought those faces grotesque with ugliness and stupidity. Now that they had grown familiar, I saw only how brave they were – ready for anything. We were the stuff heroes were made of.

The mountain trails belonged to the Naga hill-tribes. They

were the people we admired most. Prejudices against anything foreign disappeared before the sight of those extraordinary brown-limbed men and women who insisted on carrying on life in the midst of a potential battlefield. Their villages, poor simple places, stood on the crest of the mountain ridges. Their fields of rice and maize were two or three thousand feet sheer down in the valley below. The women climbed down to work and back again with their *chickos* strapped to their backs. The kids, wearing no more than a ragged waistcoat, never made a sound.

On one occasion when we were resting, during a recce, a party of Naga women overtook us and gestured that they wanted food for their children. I gave one of the women a cigarette. She gestured for the child to have one too, took it, and stuck it in her black hair. She was fairly young, lean, wearing a long skirt, barefoot.

'Speak English?' I asked.

She looked at me, a long troubling look, and said something incomprehensible. Would she have consented to have a spot of intercourse in the nearest *chaung*, buttocks sinking in the soft sand? Of course I did not make a move towards her. That night, when the moon floated above the mountains, I thought of her again and burned her out of my skull with rough fantasy.

Along the wild trails came news and rumours. The rest of 2 Div was delayed. Extra units were being flown in from the Arakan. Imphal had fallen. Imphal was holding out. The Japs were outflanking us. Kohima was surrounded. The Chindits, operating with Gurkhas and Kachins, were trying to join up with Vinegar Joe Stilwell in Northern Burma. Generalissimo Chiang Kai-shek was assassinated. Our water ration was going up soon.

Water was one of our troubles. It arrived at Brigade HQ in a water-truck, having come from the Jiri River, several miles away. It always stank of chlorine; even the *char* stank of chlorine. When you watered the rum ration with it, the rum stank of chlorine. Water was always short. We shaved and washed in one mug-full each morning – or you could shave in the dregs of your *char*, which was the only way to get warm water. Apart from that, we never washed or took our clothes off. We kept our boots and ankle-puttees on all day, to guard against typhus.

It was all a big fucking lark at first.

Belgaum had been much rougher than this. We had here, too, the interest of learning about the situation – of acquiring, for instance, the names of the Jap generals, Mutaguchi attacking Imphal, and Sato attacking Kohima, which seemed to give us an extraordinary and paradoxical intimacy with them. It was difficult to think of them in human terms; they were much more like H. G. Wells's invading Martians.

The area was now stiff with Sato's men, although our forces were building up. The Worcesters moved in next to us along the road though the rest of 2 Div was still assembling in Dimapur. We slowly gained a clearer picture of the situation. Four or five miles nearer Kohima than our positions, a defensive box was built at Jotsoma, where artillery could lay down fire on Kohima Ridge, on which the Japs had established themselves at several points – notably the Naga village. When Japs cut the road between Zubza and Jotsoma, the artillery carried on as usual.

It was on Easter Sunday that we were ordered to move down to the road behind the Japs and make contact with a detachment of the Assam Battalion which was withdrawing after holding off the Japs near Imphal. On that same day, the Mendips suffered their first casualties.

Jock McGuffie had been into the village of Zubza and reported it as a mankey, stinking hole.

'The only bloody attraction Zubza's got is a pontoon school,' Jock said. 'They're playing for fucking mepacrine tablets – let's go and show them how one evening, you and me, Stubby?' But, when the chips were down, I was infantry and Jock was not, and our paths did not cross again for several rugged weeks.

Whatever its shortcomings, Zubza was usefully situated as regards the trails, and a small outdoor church service was held there on the morning of Easter Sunday. Our blokes were strolling about openly after the service, when a Jap 75mm. opened up from Merema Ridge. A sapper officer called Lodge and two BORs were killed. From then on, we began treating the whole business as less of a game.

The foray down to the road was also no fun. We were getting some bully beef hash inside our pullovers when Major Inskipp came over with Lieutenant Boyer and addressed us. Inskipp was Company C.O., a smiling old boy with a wide face and a gaze that could go through you like a bullet when necessary. He told us that the new campaign was about to begin and that the Mendips were about to add a new name to their list of battle honours. Tonight we were simply concerned with helping the Assam Battalion to safety. Tomorrow, we should probably be allowed to kill as many Japs as we wanted – there was a good supply in the neighbourhood. The usual sort of stuff. With something touching in the way he finished with 'Good luck, boys!', as if we really were his boys.

We began to move in column file before night came down. Occasional vistas through tree-cover showed darkness rising out of the valleys, while the upper world was serene and in mellow light. It all looked so peaceful, you could hardly credit that the place was swarming with Japs. Over Mount Japvo way, black cloud was piling up. Easter fucking Sunday!

Scouts came back, we halted, spread out along a gully, squinting down through the bushes. An Indian file moved through us, heading up towards Zubza. Members of both parties gave a whispered '*Thik-hai!*' to each other in passing as if it was a code-name. The Indians left behind them the individual smell of Indian troops, sweetly rancid with a touch of wood smoke and damp.

It took us two hours to get into position near the road. By then, night was absolute and the black clouds had closed overhead.

We waited. I was stuck behind a tree trunk with the radio set, and could not even see the road, but it was somewhere just below and ahead. There was a blown bridge nearby, round a curve of the road, although it was too dark to see the curve either. Messages came through saying the Assam Regiment was on its way.

In the Assamese night, silence was never complete. Cicadas chirped, night birds called, an occasional wild dog yelped, and countless little things scuttled through the undergrowth. Something moved all the time. There was silence as well, felt like an echo in a shell, rolling down off the hilltops. Totally different from India, where you had but to kick a sacred cow and villages woke all round you. Here, the place was deserted except for the poor buggers who had to fight in it.

There was another noise. Tension all round, rifle butts gripped more firmly. A password called across the road. Men slipping across to our side. The Assamese!

Then the firing broke out. We had heard a lot of shooting from Jotsoma an hour earlier – the Japs were going in there, by the sound of it. Now came rifle and automatic fire, punctuated by shell fire, from a greater distance. That would be Kohima getting it again! It sounded like a real pitched battle.

But the Assam Battalion kept coming across the road, Kukis, Karsis, and all the other tribesmen. What was more, they formed up behind us, in proper order.

It began to rain, a dull steady downpour. But the stragglers still arrived. They had walked over the hills from Imphal, and moved without hurry or apparent fatigue.

One of them was saying something in a low excited voice, down on the road. I could hardly hear anything for the drum of rain on my monsoon cape, which was protecting the set. A minute later, Lieutenant Boyer fired a Verey pistol. As bright light broke over the scene, he gave the order to fire. The chaps lining the ditch by the road opened fire. Dusty Miller opened up on the Bren.

There were yells from the thickets opposite, and some answering fire. The Japs were there all right, and must have been on the heels of the Assamese, but they did not venture to cross the road.

Our shooting stopped, the rain petered out. The racket up at Jotsoma and Kohima was still going strong. Poor bastards! We waited for the order to move out, now that the job was done. Word came only when the survivors of the Assam Battalion were clear. We started moving up the track again. Dawn was just filtering in. Our first modest bit of action was over.

By now, Kohima had been six days under siege.

Only when you stood in that landscape, with your boots firm on the ground, could you understand why advances by either side were so slow. Whatever the country looked like from the air, from the ground it was baffling. To the confusion of whatever prehistoric calamity had thrown up this maze of small mountains and valleys, nature had added entangling forest. Every hill, valley, re-entrant, and salient was covered with vegetation which, although from a distance it looked little more than knee-high scrub – so large were the Assamese perspectives – on closer acquaintance proved to be a riot of thorn, bamboo, and towering trees. Every minor feature, nothing on a map, proved capable in actuality of swallowing a battalion. Every hillside mopped up men as a sponge mops up beer.

Every now and then, pressure on the sponge caused a trickle of combatants to emerge. Often they were walking wounded, from one of the sites within the Kohima perimeter, from Garrison Hill, the GPT Ridge, or even the disputed area by the District Commissioner's bungalow – then the most famous building in the world. They passed through our lines, V Force men, Burmese Regiment, Mahrattas, Gurkhas, Nepalese, Indian Infantry, Royal West Kents, and disappeared again into the consuming jungle, led by Naga warriors. Dimapur was far away, somewhere in the blue distance near Calcutta.

Our attention hinged on Kohima, always Kohima, and what was happening there. The Japs never gave up. Their forces and ours were practically intermingled, and often fought for days on end within a few yards of each other. Behind the D.C. bungalow, centre of the dispute, the opposing sides lobbed grenades, volley after volley, across the tennis court. The RAF and the Americans were making airdrops of food, water, and ammunition to our beleagured forces but, inevitably, some of these fell into Jap hands. It was hard to see how either side could survive for long.

There were plenty of other factors we did not understand. Why didn't Sato simply by-pass Kohima – there was nothing there anyone could possibly want, except the command of the Dimapur-Imphal road – and make for Dimapur, the gateway to India and impossible to defend? And why could we not make better progress in relieving Kohima?

The Japs had command of the road at several strategic places. To try to advance down it was to invite ambush and withering fire. It was equally impossible to move along the valley, for similar reasons: that broad valley was constantly under observation. Equally, you could not move along the ridges of the hills – they were too broken, too directionless. We were forced into the undergrowth. And the undergrowth provided the Japs with unlimited cover. They had perfected a system of interdependent bunkers which protected each other with cross-fire; if you charged one, you came under attack from two more. 2 Div was well mechanized, but mechanization counted for little here. Many of us were practising guerilla warfare before we ever heard of the term.

We were joined at Zubza by a detachment of Pathan muleteers, tall men with monstrous black animals in their charge, over a hundred strong. These cantankerous animals set off wild-eyed into the bush, bearing supplies. Our perimeter had to be extended so that we could give them protection, which caused a certain amount of ticking and grumbling. The culinary habits of the Pathans, the aroma and blood-sucking flies of their charges, made them unpopular. Besides, *mules* were so primitive. They had gone out with the Great War!

Swinton dealt with that sort of attitude when he addressed us one morning, two days after we had gone down to the road to help the Assam Battalion.

'You'll all be glad to know that 2 Div is finally moving into action. We are going to relieve Kohima. The rest of the brigade is already in the vicinity, and 5 Brigade is taking up temporary positions nearby. The First Battalion will be moving into action tonight, at midnight. The cooks are laying on an extra issue of *char*, and then we go forward.

'Naturally, we aren't too keen for the Japs to know about this. They will have their heads down by then, although we are prepared to disturb their sleep if we have to.' We laughed at his assumed consideration.

'We shall all be glad of the chance to do something positive. And we need a little exercise. We have been sitting on our arses for too long. We shall proceed to Kohima along the Merema Ridge.' He indicated it with a sweep of his arm. 'We shall move along the Ridge, clearing it of enemy as we go, and we shall deliver a hefty punch at Sato from his left, where he will be least able to deal with it, and where it will hurt him most. He may be well dug in, but we shall dig him out – even if only to give him a decent burial!

'On this operation, we have two objectives: to kill as many Nips as we can, and to relieve the Kohima garrison. I know you approve of both objectives.' We cheered to show we did. 'Good. After Kohima, things will be easier. The road will be opened to Imphal and the Chindwin, and life should be simple. This is the decisive point in the war in the Far East – so we all understand, don't we, why the Powers-That-Be had to call in the Mendips for the job!' More cheers.

'Let me just remind you about the question of supplies. They are vital, as you know. We are going to want to eat up on Merema. We may get some air-drops, but cargoes are limited. It goes without saying that the Fourteenth Army is short of planes! We are lucky to have the Pathans and their mules with us, to bring up rations and ammunition. They are absolutely marvellous chaps and we shall depend upon them absolutely. They come from mountainous regions of Pakistan and are a warrior people; they must be given every respect, for our stomachs if not our lives are in their hands.

'Good! This is not a picnic we are embarking on. You are all aware of that. We have a worthy foe, and we shall vanquish him worthily. I will remind you of the words of Shakespeare, which he gives to Henry V to speak before another great battle, the Battle of Agincourt.

' "And gentlemen in England now abed
    Shall think themselves accursed they were not here,
    And hold their manhoods cheap while any speaks
    That fought with us upon St Crispin's Day!"

'The going before us will not be easy – we never expected it would be easy – but the victory, I promise you, will be

[223]

something nobody will ever forget. We shall never forget it, and it will never be forgotten in the annals of our beloved country.'

As Swinton stood down, we cheered, and looked covertly round at one another. How many men there had tears gleaming in their eyes, as I had in mine – and have now, writing of it, all these years after! Those words from Shakespeare seemed to open up something inside us. If I ever come across them now, I can still weep, entirely without knowing why, for they bring back the emotions we felt in those shabby Assamese glades.

'Bloody good speech,' I said to old Bamber, as we dispersed.

'Old Willie's got the gift of the gab all right!'

'Fuck off, it was a bloody good speech.'

'I didn't say as it wasn't!'

'Well, don't let your enthusiasm run off with you. "As long as you're listening to speeches, you're doing nothing worse", I suppose!'

He looked at me. 'You're young, Stubby, you're a good lad. But life isn't all speeches. It isn't what you says as counts, it's what you do.'

To accompany his talk, Swinton had brought a blackboard, on which his ADC sketched a map of the battle situation. The disputed section of the Dimapur Road formed the outline of the top half of a duck afloat. Kohima was tucked into the duck's head and beak. Above the head lay Naga Village, now in Jap hands. Down below its chest and off the drawing lay Imphal and the road to Burma. Zubza lay somewhere at the highpoint of the duck's tail. Stretching in an arc from tail to Naga Village was the Merema Ridge, overlooking the road for much of its length. That was our route!

Its lower crests were above our camp, its slopes clothed in jungle, its crest hidden by false crests. Everyone looked at it and drew his own conclusions. And at midnight, as ordered, we began moving in single file up the jungle trails, heading for those false crests.

We began to learn the lesson many an army has learnt. Mountainsides eat armies. The true scale of any country can only be appreciated by walking over it. From a distance, the prospect of Merema looked straightforward. Climbing its hillsides seemed to call simply for patience and a little endurance. Yet, once we were under its tree cover, we found how every hillside was broken into dips and depressions and pimples and gulleys. Every miniature plateau offered its miniature ravines and cliffs. And, of course, Merema Ridge was just one comparatively minor feature of the area.

In daylight, thick vegetation cut visibility badly – you could walk into the Japs before you saw them. You might get a glimpse through the thickets of the crest, cloud drifting over it, and think, Thank fuck, we're there at last! You'd reach it, and it would prove to be just another false crest, and more thicket and another crest looming above you. Those bastard and everlasting hills! We didn't know what we were at – it wasn't exactly jungle warfare and it wasn't mountain warfare either. If this was Assam, roll on fucking Burma!

It was a matter of keeping going. We moved ahead for fifty minutes, had a ten minute rest, went on again. It rained hard for two hours. We wore our monsoon capes. You couldn't see where you were going and the trail grew very slippery. We could hear firing and the eternal Jap mortars, but nothing too near.

By first light, we were still stuck on the limitless hillside. Looking back through the trees, you could get glimpses of the rest of the world. It was all jungle. You could not believe that there were two brigades near you. A whole invasion force could have lost itself on Merema Ridge alone.

We dug ourselves in soon after dawn. I helped Tertis dig Gor-Blimey's foxhole while Gor-Blimey did his rounds. We ate a breakfast of eggs and soya-link and *char*. Pickets were set out, everyone else got their heads down. We were having trouble with the bloody wireless set, and it was hell to get a message back to HQ, though we picked up 5 Brigade loud and clear.

We had patrols out during the day. There was one brush with the Japs, and two of them were killed. Aircraft were flying most of the day, Dakotas and RAF planes, dropping supplies to the garrison at Kohima. And sporadic firing. Only at tiffin-time was there a sort of truce. Thank God the Japs ate lunch at the same time we did.

With dusk, we moved forward again. Forward and upward. The eternal climbing, slipping back, the possibility of losing your footing and falling on to the man behind, or the man in front falling on to you. It was like madness, your leg muscles threatening to seize up, your heart threatening to burst. Although cool came with the dark, the air was suffocating in the jungle, and we were attacked by sodding great mosquitoes that whined and hummed round your face. To begin with, you'd try to smack them out of the way, but it soon became not worth while – easier to let them feed. By morning, our faces were a mass of blotches.

But before morning we had our own bit of excitement. It was a hell of a night everywhere. Kohima was getting a plastering again. The noise came down the valley and you couldn't be sure of its direction: the great hillsides distorted everything. There was also shooting down on the road, and behind us, and above us, and to one flank. It seemed as if everyone was blazing away bar us.

We got word over the radio that a company of Japs was

attacking our former position down at Zubza. There were tanks at Zubza now, which had fired their seventy-five-millimetre guns into the Japs at almost pointblank range. The surviving Japs were now climbing towards us, and a reception committee was quickly arranged.

It was a relief travelling downhill for a change. We moved to the rear, No. 2 Platoon, through our own troops. Our rearguard was already dug in on one of the false crests. There was a spur here, and Charlie Cox and Dusty set up our Bren on it, with good vision into the jungle just below.

We waited for two hours before anyone turned up.

The Japs came up the trail, moving fast. Their scouts were bayonetted without a word, and the rest allowed to gather on the ridge before our lads opened fire. From the spur, we could pick the rest off as they tried to rush up and join battle, and we could cover the trail for some way back. Although the poor little bastards yelled and blazed away, they didn't have a hope. We killed thirty-one of them, with no more than a flesh wound among our own men.

To celebrate, we had a quick brew-up and then made our way back to our proper positions. Before we got there, messages came through from the Worcesters on our left flank that their advance patrols had encountered a cluster of Jap bunkers right on the crest of the Ridge, which was now at last not far above us. Our platoon got our heads down while arrangements were being made for an attack the next day. I slept like a corpse, forehead down on pack.

By all accounts, the next day's attack was deadly. By this time, some 2nd Manchesters were up with us – they were machine-gunners, and useful lads to have along, but on this occasion they could not bring their fire to bear properly to keep the Japs' heads down while the troops went in, since the Japs were dug in slightly above our positions. We had some help from the brigade mortars, or such as had been assembled at this height.

The lads went in after the mortars had been pumping away for twenty minutes, with the Worcesters supporting on the left flank.

One of our casualties was 'Dolly' Lazenby. Sergeant Lazenby of 'C' Company was a tough old nut who had survived all that the Krauts could throw at Dunkirk; he led his platoon in with a bag of grenades round his neck. He was shot in the leg almost at once, but managed to fling himself right under the slits of one of the Jap bunkers. He lobbed a grenade through the slit. A crafty Jap grabbed it and flung it back again at once, so that it burst among our men.

Lazenby pulled the pin out of another grenade, counted to four, and then lobbed it in. Even then, all the Japs were not killed – two had to be bayonetted before the bunker was ours. By this time, Lazenby was dead, killed by cross-fire.

The mortars had no effect at all on the Jap bunkers. After two charges, our attack was called off and we had to give up the one bunker we had gained. The Mendips had lost three men and the Worcesters, who had come up against the main complex of bunkers, six – with nothing gained. We had not even got on to the heights of the Ridge yet.

We were held up where we were all that day, in rain and shine. Now that the Japs knew our positions, they kept pounding away with their mortars; we had to keep our heads down. Part of the trouble was that we were bunched just below the escarpment, making it difficult for reinforcements to come up from below. During the afternoon, we spread out round the hillside – not without minor skirmishes, for the Japs had a nasty habit of digging foxholes in the jungle. When you stumbled over them, the bunkers above immediately gave covering fire. Those bunkers, dug well in, with roofs covered by tree-trunks and earth, were almost impregnable and almost did for us.

At nightfall, we had another try at the main Jap position. Sappers had come up with pole charges, which gave us a handy new weapon if we could get close enough to use it. These were mines on the end of a long bamboo, designed for poking into bunkers, which were proving successful at Kohima.

Before we went in, we had the benefit of R.A. support from guns at Jotsoma, a couple of miles over on the other side of the road. Once they were registered, their shells clumped home above us in heartening fashion. You lay there listening, imagining the Jap bunkers crumpling. Radio contact was good across the valley, although the R.A. could observe what they were doing better than we could. After a softening up period, another attack was launched. Our attack!

This time, No. 2 Platoon was having first bash, under Gor-Blimey. We were all there on our bellies, Geordie, Wally, 'Honey Pears' Ford, Chalkie White, Feather – the lot. Waiting for the word. We all looked really tough and dirty bastards.

The MMGs were supporting better now, since they had been dug into shallow pits in the rock. Using tracer one-in-five, they directed their fire right into the Jap bunkers, making the little bastards inside keep their scabby skulls down.

The signal came, the machine-gun fire stopped, Charley Meadows yelled at us, and we got on our hind legs and lunged forward, shouting as we went. Geordie was next to me, not showing a sign of his earlier jitters.

All that shelling, mortaring and machine-gunning hadn't put a single bunker out of action, though it had spread the jungle about the place. A few trees had come down – one on our right flank was burning into the night like a torch, and I saw Harding leap over its roots. All the bunkers began spitting out deadly fire.

At least there were shell-holes in which we could fling ourselves for cover. From them, we were able to worm our way forward and get right under the bunkers. This wasn't easy – the bunkers were built with their weapon-slits close to the ground. Inside the bunkers, any number of Japs could produce a deadly volley of grenades, machine-gun, and small arms fire with little danger to themselves. This was what they were now doing.

But we knew the lie of the land and we had the hang of things. This was going to be our fucking ridge! We were beginning as we meant to go on. We used every inch of cover, worming our way forward, firing as we went. The pole-charges, too, did their stuff. We covered the sappers as they bunged their grenades home. An explosion, fire and smoke pouring out, screams, and we'd be in there!

One by one, we disinfected the Jap bunkers, bayonetted or shot all the surviving Japs inside, and then moved on to the next. The only real hitch was when a bunker we had cleared opened fire on us again. These were well established defences, and the Japs had had a chance to establish communicating trenches between the bunkers. Once we got the idea, we killed several Japs in trenches. With every bunker that fell, the next was correspondingly easier.

The noise all the time was colossal, though you didn't realize that properly till afterwards. The Worcesters were having a tough time too, somewhere to our left flank. You hardly knew what was going on, yet all sorts of sixth senses saw to it that you worked as one of the team and avoided the flying shit. None of the Japs surrendered, scarcely a one of them fled. They stayed at their posts, where they could do most damage, until the last. It was weird to jump into the bunkers after we had blasted them open and find the enemy tumbled over the floor, his flesh and guts spattered over the walls.

Orders came that we were to hold the positions we had gained. We pitched the dead Japs over the *khud*, took over their defences, and dug new ones to the rear. We made our own latrines. After first light, our reliefs trooped in and we moved back for food and kip, shagged to the bloody wide, dead of emotion.

After four hours' sleep, I was roused and went to relieve Wally in the signal trench.

'You've been bleeding, mate,' he said. 'You want to stand further from the razor next time.'

I was so covered with crap from head to foot that I didn't know what was happening. And I was still half-asleep. Almost automatically, I took Wally's place at the wireless set, where Gor-Blimey was taking reports and orders. He looked almost as scruffy as I felt.

'Haven't you had any sleep yet, sir?' I asked between messages.

'I'm going off in a minute, Stubbs. Is your ear hurting you?'

'I don't think so, sir.'

'Get it dressed afterwards.'

One of the orderlies brought up *pialas* of hot *char* while the R/T messages went on. I just slumped there, doing what I was told. From the situation reports, it sounded as if every bloody hillside in Assam was loaded with Japs. The garrison at Kohima had had another bad night; the D.I.S. box had fallen to the Japs, who were now firing into the West Kents' perimeter. But we had wiped out almost a whole company of Japs, and it looked as if the Ridge might be clear for most of the rest of the way to Naga Village.

The regimental aid station to which I went to have my ear dressed was some way below our position. I got there after tiffin. It seemed a blessed refuge of peace. The badly wounded had been sent back from here to Zubza, and thence somehow they would have to make their way to distant Dimapur. Serious cases would then have a further journey: back to the railhead at Gauhati, across the Bramaputra, and the long exhausting journey to the hospitals in Barrackpore and Comilla, if they lived that long. India! – Unimaginably far in time and space!

My ear had been nicked by a flying wood splinter. Feeling an absolute malingerer, I had it patched, and then made my way to a rest tent, where a party was being made up for returning to our forward positions.

'Hey, Horry, some Burmese *bibi* bite your ear, then?' There sat old Di Jones, among half-a-dozen other bods, smiling at me, nodding his head, making little clicking noises under his breath.

'If there was any *kyfer* on this mountain, you'd smell it out first, Di, wouldn't you?'

Although he wore boots and puttees, his right trouser-leg had been cut away below the knee and a bandage applied round his calf.

'Just a flesh wound from a bit of grenade,' he said. 'Not enough to get me back to India.'

'You don't want to miss the excitement, do you, Di?'

He lowered his voice and said apologetically, 'This sort of business, this fighting, it's really for youngsters. I'm a bit too old. I wouldn't mind going home.'

I offered him one of my de Reskes and sat down beside him. We lit up and sat looking at the tired green foliage outside the tent. There was much I wanted to say to him.

'It'll be a better world after the war, Di, once we get the Germans and Japs out of the way.'

'Hope you're right.'

'Of course it will be!'

He said nothing.

'You're a miserable old sod, Di!'

'Let's just say I've seen more of the world than what you have, Horry.'

'I thought you'd never left the Valley till you joined the Mendips!'

'You don't have to leave the Valley to find out life's pretty tough, boy, believe you me!'

'It'll all be changed after the war. You ask Enoch Ford. It'll be a place with better opportunities and everything.'

'I hope you're right. Myself, I don't believe that, any more than I believe in Communism. See the way the gov'ment have taken control of everything, rations and coal and clothing and the lot, all since war broke out. Well, you watch if they don't keep things the same way after the war, same as they kept on passports after the last war!'

I laughed. 'There wouldn't be much point in fighting if things weren't going to be better afterwards, would there?'

One of the other bods there, also with a patched leg, had been listening to us and smoking silently. His name was Coles. He was one of the hard cases in Dolly Lazenby's platoon. He said, 'You want to read your history, mate! Wars never improve nothing for the likes of us, do they, Di-boy?'

'No, I don't think they do. Not so's you'd notice. My old man served three years in the last war and got a bayonet through the guts on Gallipoli. He came back home to ten years' unemployment. That killed him off in the end as sure as the bayonet wound . . .'

We all sat looking out at the tired green foliage outside, smoking our cigarettes in silence, until they came to collect us.

The whole battalion was moving into the previously held Jap positions, and extending them to the east. The panorama was staggering from the top of the ridge, where I found myself doing look-out duty towards sunset. We could see where the Manipur Road ran, from Zubza on. To the eastern end of the valley, Kohima Ridge was plainly visible, curving like the walls of a great dam. Its sides were a deep turbulent blue. Rain was falling there, moving to envelop us. The sun caught it, and a great rainbow came into being, rising from the hillsides of Jotsoma and Two Tree Hill, bright against black raincloud. Behind it, serene in sun, appeared Pulebadze, a fearful and indestructible wedge of mountain. The sight could have been no more striking if heavy organ music had rolled out of the hills.

There were now two miles to cover over pretty dicey terrain to the village of Merema itself, and then rather less down to the outlying areas of Naga Village. Once through that, we were almost at Kohima. How easy it is to set it down – indeed, how easy it appeared in that day of our first success, although we had had a taste of the territory and the Jap resistance.

We felt optimistic then – in Assam, our spirits were up and down pretty regularly. The Pathans and their mules were bringing the supplies up and a cookhouse was dug in against shelling and mortaring. There was no water to spare for washing.

Everyone got some rest during that day. The plan was to move again after dark, and keep up progress as fast as possible.

It took us three days to reach Merema. Even on top of the ridge, the going was virtually impossible. We kept hitting dense patches of bamboo and thorn. The monsoons were gathering, and rain hampered everything. In Assam, the rain falls in a solid lump. There were Japs about too, but no more fortified positions. Patrols we could deal with – Japs above ground were as vulnerable as anyone else: more vulnerable, because they did not have our initiative. That old Forgotten Army spectre of the Invincible Yellow Man was broken for ever. (After the war, when the British, French, Dutch, and other European nations tried to re-establish their rule over their old territories, they found that the older myth of the Invincible White Man had also been shattered for ever.)

We wanted to have a go at Merema, where a seventy-five-millimetre gun gave us a lot of trouble, but it was heavily defended and the plan was to by-pass it and press ahead towards Naga Village and Kohima beyond. This meant coming off the ridge and down into the *nullah* again.

Unfortunately, as we started to descend in pouring rain, we were ambushed by a Jap patrol. Our chaps were badly shot up and most of the Jap patrol escaped behind thickets of thorn. In no time, we got a hell of a pasting from the seventy-five-millimetre gun and from mortars. The Jap mortarmen were always deadly. A mortar exploded among some Pathans, killing two of them and sending a mule stampeding madly among the trees. It fell headlong down over the *khud*, taking a consignment of rifle oil and four-b'-two flannelette with it.

We spread out and got our heads down. In doing this, our right flank walked slap into a concealed advance bunker which had been keeping quiet until then. It opened fire with all it had got and several Mendips were killed, including old Chalkie White, who had owed Ali the *char*-wallah five rupees for eight years. So we were involved in a nasty two-cornered fight, in neither corner of which we had an advantage. A storm banged and clattered overhead, rain came down with renewed violence. I could not get anything but atmospherics out of the set. Eventually, a runner was sent back down the trail to ask for smoke, under which we could advance. The runner was killed a mile back along the trail.

We had to settle in where we were. The Japs weren't coming in to us and we could not get at them. A lousy situation. It was impossible to retreat. We had to work away with entrenching tools and dig in as best we could. There was no proper defensive position at all.

Hot soup came up as we rested. I was off the set, manning a

rifle pit with Carter the Farter, when Geordie crawled over, mess-tin full of soup in his hand, and climbed in with us.

'How did you manage to do that without spilling your fucking soup?' Carter asked.

'Oh . . . I was sort of lucky . . . I don't know . . .'

'You see, you aren't such a Jonah, Geordie!'

'I'll tell you something for nothing, my fucking feet ache, like.'

Carter began singing 'Tell me the old, old story. . .'

'Here, Stubby, mate, I killed a Jap.' His Adam's apple started bobbing again. 'I shot the poor bastard smack in the chest!'

'Shoot as many as you can. That's what we're up here for. Don't fuck about.'

Carter said, 'If you don't shoot them, Geordie, they'll fucking shoot us. That's what it's all about. If you haven't got that through your tiny Newcastle skull by now, you'd better get to Inskipp *jhaldi* and ask to go fucking home, because you're no fucking use to us.'

He looked really vicious, showing his teeth and glaring ahead over his gun barrel. Geordie stared at him and said, half in a whisper, 'You're scared too, Carter, aren't you?'

'Of course I'm fucking scared,' Carter said, still looking ahead.

Geordie drank up his soup and then crawled back to where he had come from.

By now, we had several wounded. Some of them were lying in the open and it was impossible to reach them. The Japs were firing at anything that stirred. We could only lie there and wait for dark. The set still yielded nothing but static. Word had finally got back, and some supplies were coming up, but it was still almost impossible to move. Part of the trouble was that we were hampered on our right flank by a sheer drop of cliff face.

Towards dusk, during a lull in the downpour, a levy of

Nagas appeared over this cliff face. Dug in though we were, word quickly got round. These heroic fellows had come to take the wounded away down one of their trails, inaccessible to us. With the aid of some of our own stretcher-bearers, the wounded were slowly collected.

One of our staff-sergeants, Badger Collins, was supervising this movement with Charley Meadows when they conceived an alternative plan of attack. Crawling on his belly, Charley dragged himself into the hole where I was on duty on the set next to Gor-Blimey.

'If we stay here all night, sir, the Japs are going to pound us with that seventy-five from Merema. It's just this bunker that's holding us up. If we could get two or three men on top of it, we could lob grenades inside and put it out of action, and the others would be a push-over. We've just got to get round the cliff-face. The Nagas will lead us.'

'It's a sheer drop into the valley!'

'The Nagas are managing, sir. It's not too bad – I've had a dekko. But we'll have to move at once, before it's too dark to see.'

Maybe I'd grown tired of calling 'Report my signals!' into the microphone.

'You might as well throw this set down the *khud*-side, sir! I'll volunteer to go, if that's okay with Sergeant Meadows.'

Gor-Blimey gave me one brief glance. 'All right. You stay here, Sergeant, and I'll take Stubbs.'

'No, sir, you hang on with the set. Stubbs and I'll go. It just needs the two of us.'

Charley passed me some grenades. We looked at each other; his normally soft face was rigidly set. We worked our way out of the trench on our bellies. I kept his boots in sight. The skin of my back crawled, preparing itself for Jap bullets. We hauled ourselves over the edge of the cliff almost face first – I took care not to look down into the distance.

The lip of the cliff had fallen away. There was a ledge of

sorts, and roots to hang on to. You couldn't help seeing the dangers of the situation. Once we were over the edge, we were out of the line of fire but, my God, the view was frightening! Far below, the injured were being lowered gently into the jungle. The valley bottom lay at least a thousand feet below. Across the way, Kohima Ridge stood out like a stranded ship, and the beleagured position of Kohima was also visible. Dakotas were circling it. Two of the Nagas had stayed behind and were waiting for us. One shuffled behind, one in front of us.

'*Thik-hai*, Stubby?'

'*Thik-hai*, Sarge.'

The Nagas led us immediately over a cross-path, where the footing was very slippery. We moved with our hands against the rock, sideways, a nasty drop below our heels. This side of the Jap defences was so sheer that they had not fortified it. With luck, we could get on top of the advance bunker and lob grenades in without being spotted from other bunkers.

I unglued my eyes from the muddy cliff-face and looked at the Naga beside me. He smiled encouragement – young, a soft face, pretty, almost girlish. The girlishness was emphasized by strings of beads round his neck and an orchid in his hair. Christ, it was a girl! – A fucking Naga pusher, climbing about as cool as you like! I nearly fell into the *khud* in sheer surprise!

Her throat, the line of tit under her tunic – for that sort of thing we were staying alive.

She motioned me on and after what seemed like an hour we went scrambling up a bank and into thick bamboo, Charley and I on our own. Two yards from the cliff and you wouldn't have known the drop existed. As we crawled among the foliage I could feel ants scampering on to my neck. I could not see what lay ahead for the sergeant's arse in my way. He moved slowly, although the platoon was now putting down covering fire, so that it was unlikely anyone would hear us. Then we were climbing on to the top of the bunker, well camouflaged by earth and growing things – which would have instantly seized hold even if they had not been planted there.

'Get over a firing-slit – pin off, lever away, count three, throw in fast, get down!' Charley said. We looked at each other with a quick glance, then worked forward. We lay ready, Charley raised his hand, and in a moment our covering fire ceased. I leaned forward, pulled the pin, flung the grenade through the aperture below. Charley yelled as he bunged his in. As I flung my grenade, I heard the little sods below me shout out and presumably make a dive for the pineapple. It exploded, Charley's exploded, the logs beneath us heaved and jarred our bodies. We hung on, thinking our last moment had come.

Yelling, our lads made a great charge forward, while Charley and I lay where we were.

So the bunker was ours in the last quarter-hour of daylight. By the look of its late inhabitants, we saw they had been diving for the grenades – their faces were cut to paste. Charley and I gazed at each other and nodded curtly. I put a couple of bullets into one little sod who was trying to bring his rifle up, despite half a hand missing.

The Japs had been manning a Taisho, a light machine-gun which had caused us a lot of discomfort. Our grenades had done no more than buckle its stand. We turned this light machine-gun on the nearest support bunker. Although we could not do much damage, we could make the marksmen keep their heads down. Our sections advanced and stuck pole-charges into the bunker – we watched them do it, and saw one of the sappers shot down from concealed firing-lines.

Although the situation had now greatly improved, we were still stuck on the lousy hillside. With all the Japs in the jungle alerted to us, there was no question of moving on till we had mopped this bit of trouble up, so we just stayed where

we were and waited. The two Nagas who had guided us –
perhaps it was a man and his daughter – picked up a few Jap
souvenirs from the advance bunker and departed, smiling
and making the thumbs-up sign.

'They were head-hunters a couple of generations ago!'
Gor-Blimey said reverently.

There were picks and shovels in the advance bunker, as
well as a litter of filth. Badger Collins got a party of us to
dismantling part of the front of the bunker. It seemed almost
impossible at first, but once we had one timber out, we were
able to break open a crude doorway. We fortified the rear
and could use the bunker as stronghold and HQ. Under
cover of dark, communicating trenches were dug. Now our
position was more secure.

Everyone was shagged out. As many men as could be
spared got their heads down. It was a question of sleeping
under monsoon capes where you lay. I found sleep came as
soon as I shut my eyes. Even in sleep, you went on endlessly
fighting – I must have climbed on to that bunker fifty times.

Our patrols reported more Japs moving in from Merema
as reinforcements. Just past midnight, I was roused and went
back to the wireless set, which was now in the bunker. We
were receiving a Strength Five signal from Brigade. Orders
came over that we were to move on immediately and remember our real objective, Kohima. Our officers swore;
officers at the rear never understood the problems of the men
under fire. Brigadier Grey ought to come and have a *shufti*
at this little lot for himself. The whole shagging mob of Base
Wallahs in New Delhi ought to be dragged from their chota
pegs and dropped into Assam.

There was nothing for it – we were going to have to go
round and not through this collection of Japs. Orders were
orders.

The trick was to disappear without letting the enemy know
your next intentions – not too difficult in thick jungle at

night. Everyone was roused. Leaving a rear detail to fire on till the last, we slipped into the bush more craftily than Sato himself. The rain had cleared, the night was fine. Over the way, Kohima was still taking punishment.

As we were withdrawing, a horrible voice woke over the jungle.

'Hello, Johnny! Hello, Johnny! Give up the battle, go away from this country. Go back to the UK or you get kill! Go back to London, Johnny!'

They had a loudspeaker in operation. We learned that members of the INA, the so-called 'Indian National Army', were working with the Japs. They were allowed to use loud-hailers, even if the Japs would not trust them with rifles.

Later, the voice broke into crazy singing. 'It's a long long way to Tipperary, It's a long long way ago, It's a long long long to Tipperary To Tipperary ago. . .' The temptation to blast away in the general direction of the voice was almost irresistible. At least it helped cover our withdrawal.

To this foul music, we moved off into the night, down a precipitous trail – led again by the Nagas.

By mid-day, after some kip, we were feeling in good shape again. This was 18 April, a memorable day. 'A' Company had dug itself in on a saddle of ground overlooking the *nulah* towards Kohima itself and protected from higher ground above us by a false crest. Patrols were posted, of course, but those off duty got a chance to rest up a bit, clean rifles, and get themselves bandaged if necessary. We could dry out our blankets, for it was a spectacular and hot morning, the sun blazing down and not a cloud in sight.

I woke feeling ghastly and dragged myself off to have a shit in the latrine trench, which had been built behind a ruined *basha*. There was a certain pleasure, generally, in squatting and smelling the raw meat stink of one's own turds, but I had a touch of dysentery now, and that was hardly enjoyable at all. When I dragged my pants down, the sight almost made me sick. I had ripped the skin of my right leg off from knee to ankle on a rock. My trousers were scarcely torn. Blood was caked everywhere, and the leeches were at me, little grey bastards that fattened up to a dull purple like a plum until you burnt them off. I applied the hot end of a cigarette and saw them fall away. I squidged them underfoot. If you rashly pulled them off, their heads stayed embedded in your flesh and an ulcer formed which could eat away your muscle and bone – the 'Naga Sore' it was called.

While I was getting myself patched at the first-aid post, the mules came up with the supplies: water, food, mail, ammo, and the rest. The old Pathans did a wonderful job. They brought big cans of fags too. Ernie Dutt issued me with two packets.

'What, de Reskes again, Ernie? Can't you do better than that?'

'These are special, boy – present from the base-*wallahs* at Delhi.'

'What sacrifices they are making on our behalf!'

'Yes. They've been saving this issue for us ever since the Great War.'

He could have been right. The paper on the de Reskes was a pale brown, the tobacco a pale green. But we sat back and smoked them and enjoyed them. We had acquitted ourselves well, had not been too badly mauled, and Kohima was very near. Its relief was not far off, after almost a fortnight of siege.

'By Christ!' Dusty Miller said, 'We deserve more medals than fucking Sato's had NAAFI suppers!'

One of our look-out posts was picturesquely sited behind a spur of rock, festooned with creeper, which stood on the edge of an escarpment. I was put on the noon-till-two watch with

Feather, and we had a good view across to Kohima through the thick afternoon heat. We could see some action round Garrison Hill and the D.C.'s bungalow, at the centre of the redoubt. It looked a complete shambles because, under constant bombardment, the area had been denuded of cover. The trees were mere stumps, some of them smouldering like spent matches. On some of the stumps, gay fabrics hung. These were parachutes used in the air-drops, and they lent an inappropriate air of festivity to the scene, as if the Japs had caught the D.C. holding a fete in his back garden.

'Look at it all!', Feather said. 'It doesn't seem real! How the hell are we going to settle down in Civvy Street again after seeing this lot?'

'You'll forget all about it once you're back on the farm again.' He had a little fruit farm in Kent.

Feather shook his head. 'After all this, I don't know how I'll settle down again with my old woman, I'm sure.'

'I shouldn't start worrying about that until you get home!'

He shook his head again.

The 2 Div guns opened up on the Japanese positions on the other side of Kohima so suddenly that we both jumped. You would wonder how anyone survived unless you had seen the bunkers.

RAF fighter-bombers were having a duffy too.

After a while, there was activity down on the road, of which we could glimpse one short stretch. We saw jeeps go by. Perhaps the road was open all the way at last. We saw dust rising, and in a minute tanks were visible. On the ridge opposite us there was movement, where columns of infantry – the Punjabis, we found later – were fanning out on to higher ground. Behind the tanks was a transport column, our transport! Old Jock McGuffie would be there somewhere, if he had not managed to bum his way back to Calcutta.

Feather nudged me and indicated something to his side of the rock. I peered over his shoulder. On one of the trails that ran below our position, several hundred yards away, a column of Japs was moving, taking no trouble to conceal themselves and chatting to each other as they went along. But what amazed us was what was with them. They had an elephant at the rear of the column. Feather slithered back to get the guard corporal, Warry Warren. Warry fetched Lieutenant Boyer. Word spread. Soon everyone who was spare was lining the edge of our escarpment, staring down at the elephant, toy-like in the distance. It was plodding along steadily, a ten-pounder gun on its back, with little Japs leading it.

'It may have come from one of the Burmese logging camps as part of the spoils of war,' Boyer said.

As we watched, two or three of the Japs threw up their hands and collapsed. The rest immediately fell to the ground. Only then did the sound of a long burst of Bren-fire reach us. Someone had the trail dead in range, and had perhaps been waiting for the Jap party to reach the best firing point: 5 Brigade, the Dorsets, very likely. The elephant raised its trunk to trumpet. Now the soldiers were on their feet again and running. One went plunging over the *khud*. The elephant toppled to its knees. It waved its trunk about, opening its mouth wide. Then it too fell over the edge and was lost to view. The firing stopped. Nobody was to be seen, unless you counted one dead body.

'Rotten fucking bastards, killing an innocent animal!' Jackie Tertis said.

'It wasn't innocent – it was an enemy elephant!', Bamber said.

We fell back roaring with laughter. Everyone just stood, looking at their muckers and bellowing with laughter. Modern warfare, air-lifts and everything, and fucking Sato was using elephants! The contrast was too much for us!

What a scene that was! What a group we were! Others had been killed or wounded – we survived and we had complete trust in each other. We worked as a machine – hadn't we proved that? All the training, all the ritualization of speech, had prepared us for this amazing, marvellous unity. Every fucker there loved every other fucker. The hierarchical structure of the British Army had triumphed over the class structure of the British; the difference between them came like illumination: class divides, is meant to divide; hierarchy unites, is meant to unite. Officers, NCOs, men, from the old Brig downwards, we were all comrades-in-arms.

So I have to put it in clumsy words now, a quarter of a century and more since we came down from those barbaric hillsides, and so I think it was. At the time it came to me like a revelation out of the clear air, without words. It was the mystique of battle. Once you have experienced it, you never forget it.

That evening, after a gruelling slog up and down the jungle-covered hillsides, after crossing the Manipur Road, the Mendips moved over the I.G.H. Spur and took up defensive positions alongside the Punjabis. We were in Kohima!

What should have been an hour of triumph was a time of utter disgust.

One of the constant disappointments of the campaign was the way in which magical names turned out to be illusion. Later, there were Palel, Tamu, Sittaung, Tiddim, Kalewa, and Schwebo – syllables which proved themselves capable of rolling thrillingly right down a lifetime – and one by one these places, like Kohima, turned out to be little more than ruined bungalows, a few burnt-out *bashas*, a tin shack, and a temple. Our positions at Kohima were scarcely as much as that: just a few pimples of hills overlooked by enemy positions and the District Commissioner's bungalow in its pock-marked grounds!

A fortnight of siege, of attack and counter-attack, had turned Kohima into a minor Somme. As 'A' Company worked its way through the shattered trees, the slanting sunlight appeared to shift and tremble. The flies were there. This was their campaign! They feasted where human beings starved. And so many varieties of fly, little dun flies that no amount of gluttony could make fat, big flies that crawled everywhere like legged grapes, scintillating flies, flies that flicked their wings as they sipped, flies that would not go away, that returned twenty times to the very same spot on your face if you struck at it twenty times, perverted flies, drunk flies, dying flies, sportive flies. They made a patina over every single thing, and could dim the daylight when they rose in their swarms.

What they fed and bred on were the pieces of human being that rotted in the churned mud. The whole site was mud, gouged by shells and trenches and running boots; bits of men, whole limbs, had been blasted all about the area. The dead bodies, fat and blackened in the heat, had at last been dragged away; but the bits that had fallen off, or had been blown off or shot off or chopped off, still lay about, and poisoned the air with their stomach-curdling sweet stench of carrion. Some of the chaps were spewing their rings up as we dug ourselves in. Fortunately, the Jap sniping intensified, which kept our minds off the butcher's compost all round.

There were all sorts of other shit lying around, as well as shit itself – boxes, boots, shattered rifles, fragments of parachute, keys, a typewriter, bottles, bandage, kit-bags – you name it. Tertis found a little brass Buddha which he rubbed up on some flannelette and kept. A couple of days later, standing watching in a trench during a torrential downpour, I spotted a curious object in the mud just ahead of me. It looked like part of an ivory bracelet. I reached forward and

tried to pick it up. It was a crescent of teeth, sticking out of a
bit of lower jaw.

I nearly went spare. Somehow, it was just too much. My
mind flipped, and I was falling through the cracks of existence
into a world where tiny yellow dentists swarmed under-
ground like worms, extracting people's jawbones through
their gaping mouths. I was with them, another gaping mouth.
Years later, that ghastly moment returned to me in night-
mares over and over again.

At the time, I did not recognize Chota Morris and the
other blokes who piled on to me to stop me screaming and
running wildly about. I didn't recognize anything but panic.
Mercifully, Chota Morris clipped me on the jaw and almost
laid me out. When I came round properly, I was sitting
propped against a tree, with several anxious faces staring
down at me, Chota's included.

'*Thik-hai*, Stubby?'

'*Achibar*, mucker. Roll on the boat that takes me home!'

'You had us fucking worried there for a moment, mate!
We thought you'd gone proper *puggle*. Geordie's off to get
you a mug of *char*.'

It was hell on that bastarding hill. The garrison had been
relieved, the position, so vital to the road from Dimapur to
Imphal – where 4 Corps were still fighting on – was held.
But all round it lay dozens of natural fortresses where Sato
and his fiendish soldiery could hold out for years. Thank God
we did not know then that we were to be stuck in that frightful place for all of five weeks. The siege of Kohima was off;
the battle for Kohima was still on.

The Japs never gave an inch. Although they were no
longer the superhuman devils of the jungle they had been to
the bods in the Arakhan, their courage and tenacity had
something supernatural about it. They did not know when
they were beaten. They launched bayonet charge after
bayonet charge, running to certain death. They shouted and

[247]

shrieked at us after dark. They never took prisoners, they never surrendered. We longed to blow their faces off their skulls, and at the same time we were proud that they were ten times more terrible than anything the Wehrmacht had to offer.

Their snipers and mortar-men kept our heads down all the time. When you moved anywhere, you moved at the double, in fear for your life. Nights were hell – night or day, for all those five weeks, none of us ever notched up more than four consecutive hours of sleep. Of course you did learn to sleep whenever there was a spare minute. Not that if felt much like sleep; it was full of things moving, and you woke feeling as if whiskers were growing on the inside of your skull.

And what were we battling for? Most of the time, we were battling for possession of the D.C.'s tennis court. Or were we battling for Burma – a country that no one in their right minds had heard of before or since!?

Perhaps you could now construct a symbol out of that tennis court and make it stand as a monument to the futility of the Forties. Where the tea-planters of Assam, in the mellow Thirties afternoons, had lobbed tennis balls over the net, we now lobbed grenades. But, at the time it was deadly imperative for us to take that innocuous patch of ground, to blast out of existence the bunkers that lay on the other side of it, and thus to open up the road below the beak of Swinton's imagined duck and clear the way south to Imphal and victory.

Somehow we lived through it all, somehow we survived on a pint of water a day and an occasional tot of rum and meagre rations, somehow we kept back fear, somehow we survived the slow loss of our muckers. Carter the Farter came back from Field Ambulance with his arm bandaged, looking all fresh and smart, kidding us about our beards and how we smelt, and that very day fell beside me with his head askew and the life-blood pouring out of his throat.

April passed, May came. More of our lads got killed –

steady old Di Jones, who had already had a wound on Merema, never to see his Welsh valley again, and his mucker, Taffy Evans, and too many other good men who stood at their posts to the last. Still we were stuck there.

One bit of the perimeter would give. We would get it back. Then another would go. The tanks came up, but could not decide the issue. Desperate fighting went on in Naga Village. Our gunners back at Zubza and Jotsoma kept plastering the heights from which the Japs plastered us. The fighter-bombers came blasting up the valley day after day. Still nothing changed. The grape-vine said that the Japs were all starving at their posts and dying of every imaginable disease, especially the yaws, scurvy, starvation and syphilis. We had killed thousands of the bastards. But their bunkers still spewed out flying steel as unremittingly as ever.

Our days up on Merema Ridge now seemed a bygone dream, a boy scout's lark. You didn't dare think how many engagements like this there would be before the Nips were pushed back into Burma, let alone out of Burma and into the oceans beyond. Nobody thought of the future, or remembered the past.

The bags of mail from home arrived regularly. All the family wrote to me in turn, sending me as lavish a ration of news and love as possible. But the world had turned inside out. Their words came from a place we could not reach to a setting they could not visualize. Amid our dirty-arsed stand-tos, home and its people faded to myths; the Japs were a hell of a fucking sight more real.

In May, with the rains settling in heavily, things began to give a bit. By the 13th, though the tennis court still held, some of the obstacles to the south fell into our hands. For the first time, we were treated to the sight of Japs running away. We cheered then, jumped out of our trenches against orders, and fired at the bastards as they went. Their figures flopped like puppets among the dismasted palms.

[249]

The rumours were proving true. The Japs were becoming demoralized, were starving, although they were never to run out of their own savage version of courage. Sato could not hold out for ever. On 1 June, his men began to pull away from their beautifully-placed positions. Before that, we had had to undergo another spasm of fighting.

The tennis court was left to the Dorsets, and welcome they were to it. On 24 May, our battalion moved south of the Kohima defences, and was set to climb Aradura Spur as a final test of stamina. This we did through thickest jungle, in pissing rain. Assam gets about twenty times as much rain as Britain, collecting most of it in three months. Most of it hit us. I was shitting six different kinds of dysentery at the time, and everyone else was practically *puggle* with weariness, illness, or jungle sores.

'A' Company was Tac. We were labouring upwards through the dripping undergrowth, while the path we followed was turning into a considerable stream. All the flies and ants of Aradura were clinging to us for safety, when some wag up the front called out a variant of our old catchphrase: 'While you're climbing up Aradura Spur you're doing nothing worse.'

Forty officers and men started pissing themselves with laughter. Progress stopped as we lay there in the gudge, helpless with mirth.

We knew there was fighting to be done when we got to the top – but, Christ, the getting there! We were going up that spur for ever! As Dusty Miller said, the jungle was so thick you couldn't tell your arse from your elbow. You couldn't see ahead or behind or sideways. Massive trees reared overhead. The radio was not operating, so we were cut off from the Royal Berks, who were supposed to be somewhere on our flank. Our whole battalion was advancing in single file, against all the rules of warfare.

The sodding soggy hillside was pitted with ravines. We

went down into one, then had to climb again. We never appeared to advance. Birds ran through the undergrowth like rats. Of course we were lugging our ammo, machine-guns, mortars, and the whole *subcheeze* with us. That day cured me of mountaineering for good.

Towards evening, the rain laid off, the sun appeared, the clouds scudded away to the Bramaputra to draw up fresh loads for the next day. This was not the true monsoon, merely what the Wogs called the *chota barsat*, or 'little rains'. Everyone realized that the Japs had to be cleared out before the monsoons finally broke.

Steaming slightly, we dug ourselves into a defensive box for the night. Anything was a relief from climbing. We brewed up *char* on our Tommy cookers and ate bully beef and biscuits from our personal rations. Then we got our heads down, and again came that peculiarly stunned sleep, where the body lay in something approaching *rigor mortis* and the mind stumbled along just below consciousness, always alert for danger, imagining horrors and terrible things coming up out of the mud. I never dreamed of home or sex. There was not even that escape from the present.

Sex was in abeyance. During the night, I was hauled out for my spell on guard. My guts were twisting and writhing with the dysentery and I wondered if perhaps a wank might cheer things up. I felt my prick in the dark. It and my balls had shrunk to almost nothing. My ballbag was a little hard wrinkled thing, pathetically trying to turn itself into armour-plating against mortar-fire. I cudgelled my brain for fant-asies, for pictures of brothels stuffed with gleaming fannies, but everything had been scoured dry. There was nothing left of me but the soldier.

Next day, the trail went winding ever upwards, the bloody jungle kept growing. I got a Strength Two chirp out of the Royal Welsh, who were also climbing the shitheap to the top; they were uncertain of their whereabouts. Major Inskipp came and spoke to us, cheering us and saying that it was not far to the top of the Spur, and that the Pathans were bringing Lifebuoy flame-throwers up to help us burn the Japs out of their bunkers. Inskipp was as filthy as the rest of us. We looked every inch a forgotten army.

This was another back-breaking day. The sodding rain came down again and never stopped. You just wanted to lie down and die. Afterwards – even long afterwards – you couldn't tell anyone what it was like.

'Where were you in the war?'

'I was in Burma.' Adding to yourself, 'Fuck my bloody luck!'

About noon, the *khud*-side was at its steepest. Nobody could move forward; it was just impossible. We were shagged out. We had to stop. Stopping was a matter of getting your crutch round the base of a tree, so that you didn't fall back on to the next bloke. All the time, there was the dread that Japs would materialize out of the foliage to one side or other, and shoot us all up. Heads down to protect our fags from the rain, we sucked at de Reskes and stayed within the defensive perimeters of our own skulls, saying nothing. There was fuck all left to say.

Firing broke out somewhere above us – how far, it was impossible to tell, and if you looked you could see nothing, just the water falling at you in great shards from the leaves above. The firing was nothing to do with us.

We'd have been there still if a scout had not come slithering back down the trail to tell us that they had at last found the top of the ridge. The firing was coming from somewhere up there. Presumably we were so late that the other units had gone in without us.

'Come on the Mendips! Let's get up this bloody hill!' Inskipp shouted. He pressed ahead himself and we followed.

The rain redoubled its efforts too. The crest remained miles ahead. The firing was lost in the drumming of water and the squelch of boots.

The jungle thinned. A miniature cliff loomed, water pouring off it in yellow streams. Orchids grew among the trees like weeds. Our forward patrol had fixed a rope to a tree, and we pulled ourselves up by it, fanning out as we got to the top, running, falling into position with weapons at the ready.

More wilderness confronted us. You could not tell where we were. Still nothing could be seen more than seventy yards ahead, although the jungle had thinned. The Japs might be lying in wait, about to open up on us with all they'd got. A plane roared overhead. How we envied the bastard snug up there in his cabin, heading for a cosy mess, way back at Jorhat or Dimapur. Remember Dimapur? Dimapur had *charpoys* and showers and beautiful canteens.

No one opened fire on us. We advanced again, in line now, Inskipp leading. The jungle closed in. We were forced back into single file. The track No. 2 platoon was following started winding away to the left, separating us from the others, and we had to retrace our steps, fucking and blinding as we went. The other platoons had their own troubles. We had to reform, rest, go ahead, again in single line. After two hours and four rests, we found the ground beginning to rise again. We still weren't at the top of Aradura!

The wireless was yielding nothing, however much I fiddled with the bloody thing during rest periods. I could cheerfully have thrown it over the *khud*-side. I knew the blokes were willing me to get in touch with someone, one of our other companies, Brigade, anyone. Gore-Blakeley sat by me in the slit-trench staring grimly into the jungle. Occasionally, he would say, without turning his head, 'Keep trying!' But we could not raise anyone. We were just plain fucking lost on Aradura.

We kept moving during the afternoon. The rain kept coming down, firing was maintained sporadically in the distance. Night fell, and the next day we moved on again, at once stiff and limp. Rations were getting low. We were running out of fags and water. We had the feeling that everyone had forgotten about us. Ominously, the firing had ceased, except for an odd round now and again.

The weather improved towards mid-morning. The jungle still dripped even when the rain stopped. We halted in a sort of clearing for a bite of tiffin. A new awfulness crawled inside my blouse. I pulled the blouse off, and a stubby centipede in twelve grey segments fell to the mud. I plonked my boot down and ground it into mush. My chest was covered with dull red blisters.

'That's all you needed, mate – the fucking pox!' Ernie said.

I let my blouse dry off on a bush while we had another shot at raising someone. This time, we managed to pick up a section of the Welch Fusiliers, Strength Three. Gore-Blakely got a report through, gave them our position as far as it could be established, and asked for the message to be relayed back to Battalion. The Welch had nothing good to report: they had reached the top of the Spur, only to encounter the Japs in strength. They had gone in more than once, but against well sited bunkers it was hopeless, and they had suffered heavy casualties. Yes, there was artillery support, but nothing had any bloody effect against those fornicating Jap bunkers.

The mere fact of being in touch with the outside world was something. We heaved ourselves to our feet and moved on once more.

It was on the next day that we finally reached the highest ground. We were no more than half-a-mile off course. Our forward patrol made contact with the Japs, who cut loose with withering M.G. fire. Even that had the effect of raising our spirits – better to fight the bastarding Japs than the jungle. Against the jungle you could never win.

But could you win against the Japs? We had our doubts.

You could not see the sods, so well were they dug in, and so torrential the rain.

We had climbed three-thousand feet of muddy mountain. Now we were fucking well expected to fight.

Being above the great hillside, we found R/T reception was better. The link opened up properly and we learned that the rest of the battalion was close at hand. Within minutes, we had contacted them. What a bloody relief! All parties had suffered the same total aggs we had, and 'C' Company had taken a hell of a mauling from a platoon of Japs, encountered on a ridge. Good news was that rations were coming up to us.

But the rain came down worse than ever. You couldn't do a thing. You could hardly breathe. The air was water. Every man had prickly heat, which the rain stung and soothed by turns. I could feel my toes rotting off in my boots. It was so impossible that the attack was postponed for the day.

Inskipp came along to break the news to us. 'I'm sorry to tell you all that the ENSA show due to be held up here to-night has also had to be postponed.' That got a laugh.

Dusty Miller called out 'While you're watching ENSA you're doing nothing worse.'

We made the best of things, digging in, making drainage trenches, spreading our monsoon capes over the foxholes.

Early next morning, we went in.

Our objective was Peter, a pimple on Cuckoo Spur, which was an outcrop of Aradura and commanded the road. While the artillery from the valley was pounding Peter, we had soup and rum. Somehow we found the strength to fight.

It was bloody murder. I had shed the set, and went in firing the sten from the hip, shouting like fuck, with Feather on one side, bayonet fixed, yelling too, and Ernie the other side, heaving grenades to make the bastards keep their heads down. But they just plastered us with fire, safe in their bunkers. We were charging uphill, perfect targets.

[255]

Dave Feather went down almost immediately. Dutt and I just charged on, but it was madness, screams coming everywhere. We were within a few yards of the bunkers when Ernie staggered over. I could see the bunker-slits, see the tongues of fire, coming right at me. I fell by Ernie.

He had been wounded in the leg, through the thigh, and was sobbing incoherently. I grabbed up his grenades and started to throw them hard as I could at the firing-slits in the bunker ahead. There was cross-fire from another bunker. Our charge withered away. It felt as if all the Japs in creation were firing at us. At me.

They hit poor old Ernie again as he lay. I felt the bullets rip into him. He never made another sound. He had always been a quiet man.

I was just possessed. Nothing meant anything. Ernie's body gave me some shelter. I went on flinging grenades. By luck, I got one through a firing-slit. I was near enough to hear their shouts. There was an explosion, screams. Then their fucking Taishio opened up again. Perhaps one of the little sods had deliberately fallen on the grenade and saved his buddies' lives.

So much for our attack! Fuck Aradura, fuck its very name, and fuck every scab-devouring sod who suggested we should climb the cunting thing! I stayed where I was, scooping a shallow trench for myself behind Ernie's body. What had happened to the rest, I hardly knew. After a bit, I heard Gor-Blimey's whistle, then his voice calling, 'Stay put and you'll be okay! Keep your heads down!'

He must have been fucking *puggle* to believe I was capable of lifting my head one bastarding inch! I was not the only one stuck in no-man's land, and a second attack would be coming soon. I stayed where I was, as ordered, clinging to the gudge. The firing had died, except for regular bursts from either side intended to keep heads down. This is what reports call 'a lull in the fighting'.

[256]

'B' Company, operating along a *nula* to one side of us, had been having mixed fortune. They found themselves facing new trenches, in which the Japs had set up one of our captured twenty-five pounders. 'B' Company charged and managed to overcome this position, gaining possession of the gun. A Jap counter-attack had been fended off, and one section dragged the gun away while the rest fought off another counter-attack. Heavy mortar-fire was brought to bear by the Japs, and many of our men were wiped out, including Captain Morgan, but the rest had been able to manoeuvre the gun and some shells round to our section of the line. Under Inskipp's command, they manhandled the gun into place. It now began blasting away at those sodding Jap bunkers at almost point blank range.

Before it registered, shells appeared to be falling all round me. I retreated under Ernie Dutt's body in terror. At that moment, I almost did my nut, like the time I found the teeth in the shit at Kohima, but a tremendous explosion jerked me back to what then passed for my senses. The same bunker into which I had thrown the grenade was going up in flames. The Japs must have had a store of petrol in it. My bowels were emptying into my trousers. A little crap more or less would make no difference.

Our brave old lads were getting set for another charge. The M.G.s were concentrating on one set of bunkers, the twenty-five-pounder on another. The range was maybe forty yards. Surely to Christ, the fucking Japs couldn't stand too much of that!

But directly we were up and running, that impossible deadly stream of fire came at us again. We ran on. You had to run on. There was fuck all for it but to run on. Fire and fucking run on!

I wasn't aware of myself getting up and plunging forward. It just happened. I saw – it all registered afterwards – Jackie Tertis's baby face contorted in a yell of fury and, beyond him, Geordie Wilkinson, mouth shut, charging on. Even as I caught sight of Geordie, he was gone, spinning round, falling. It meant nothing. I charged on with the others.

A second bunker had been blasted open and was half-collapsed. Some genius got a Mills bomb into it, and suddenly it was erupting Japs. They came pouring out of the earth itself, black and smoking. I heard myself yelling – fuck knows what, 'Kill!' probably!

They were big buggers, not the little bow-legged guys of legend.

They were – shag me, the cheeky cunts were putting their fucking hands up, sticking their hands up, fucking surrend-ering, the bastards! *Surrendering!* We shot them down as they appeared. As I made it to the bunker with Enoch close beside me, a Jap officer popped his head up, sword in hand. Maybe he was going to surrender it. He was quite spick and span, with a trim little moustache.

'Get the bastard!' Enoch yelled. We dived together.

The three of us went sprawling across the earth. The Jap half-rose, we grabbed him, and with our combined weights fell back into the ruined bunker. Partly smothered in mud, I saw he was fighting to draw his revolver. But Enoch had him by the throat and was choking the life out of him. I grabbed his wrist, wrenching his arm backwards until something cracked.

Gor-Blimey came up, panting like a dog.

'I'm knackered,' he said. Blood was streaming down his face from a cut on his temple. He swayed on his feet. After a moment, he recovered. With eyes half-shut he said, 'Secure this officer and see he does not escape. He must not be ill-treated. The other bunkers . . .'

He slipped down against the bank. We saw there was blood all over his tunic.

'Hang on to this bastard,' Enoch said.

As I sat on the Jap officer, Enoch ran down to Gor-Blimey

and dragged him in to our position of relative safety. We could see then a ragged wound in Gor-Blimey's chest. He opened his eyes, looked at us, and belched up blood. His hands fluttered and he lay still.

'Oh Christ!' I heard myself say. 'They've killed dear old Gor-Blimey!'

'Well, we'll settle this fucker's fucking hash for him!' Enoch said. He jumped up and thrust his bayonet into the Jap officer, right up to the hilt, until it squelched.

The firing was still going on, the twenty-five-pounder blasting away whenever it had a line-of-fire, although Jap mortars further back were now responding. All told, we took care of twenty more bunkers, main ones and auxiliaries. Some time during the melée, the long awaited Lifebuoys came up, and we burned the bunkers out. It was a massacre. After a while, we began to take prisoners.

By the end of the long bloody afternoon, Peter was ours. We had a string of thirty prisoners, tied in a line, hands behind backs, with their own signal wire. The rumours had been true. The Japs were in a far worse state than we were, filthy, starved, diseased. Many of them had a fever and looked at death's door; but as long as they had been able to stand, they had been able to lean to and fire out of their bunkers. Brave bastards, brave to the last! – And fucking stupid too.

Jackie Tertis and I were rounding them up into some sort of shit-order. Tertis was staggering about almost as much as the Japs, and looked almost as black and ragged.

'How're you doing, Jackie, mate?'

He grinned at me, and was no longer baby-faced. With a would-be playful gesture, he swung the rifle to point at my guts. 'I'm doing all fucking right. What did you expect? I can look after my fucking self. And I'll tell you something for nothing – if one of these fucking slant-eyed pricks here makes a wrong move, I'll shoot the cunt in two!'

Our pathetic prisoners stood before us with drooping shoulders, plainly expecting to be blown to hell at any moment. None of them made a move.

'Get stuffed, Tertis! This lot's fucking had it.'

'Just let them try it on, that's all, and I'll shoot the cunts in two.'

'This bunch of heroes can hardly stand, never mind run.'

'I'll shoot the cunts in two!'

He swung his rifle up as if to do what he said. The Japanese bent their heads and swayed slightly, as if facing a stiff breeze.

We'd hoped for a good night's rest, but mortars were pounding our positions. For a while, it looked as if we might even have to withdraw. But 'B' Company somehow managed a sortie by moonlight, thinned though its ranks were, and clobbered one mortar position. We slept, and in the morning had a go at one last group of three bunkers that had somehow escaped detection. The Japs put up little resistance and we bagged some more prisoners. They were meek and respectful, standing about with bowed heads. The shit had been knocked out of them. They cowered before Tertis.

Our doctors attended everyone. Stretcher parties were busy loading casualties on to the backs of the mules for the hellish journey down to the road. Even there, their troubles would be only just starting; the hospitals of Comilla and Barrackpore were a dismaying journey off.

Freed from the wireless set for a couple of hours, I should have got my head down, but for once weariness had gone too far for sleep. I wandered over to the mules, exchanging grins with the Pathans, and there was Geordie Wilkinson, painfully lashed over one of the largest, blackest brutes.

'Geordie, old mate!'

He looked ghastly. His face was dead white, its tan washed

away. His entire uniform was dark with blood. The bandage round his stomach was soaked with blood. Another bandage round his upper leg was cleaner, although there too the blood was beginning to show.

He opened his eyes. I stood by him, trying to smile at him. 'Do you want a fag, mate? How about a Blighty Players?'

He moved his head. His eyes closed again and he said, quite distinctly, 'They got me in the guts, mucker ... I reckon I'm a sort of goner, like.'

I took his hand. 'You'll be okay, Geordie. They'll patch you up. We'll all see you down on the road. The Japs are packing it in, did you know that? They've had their fucking chips.'

'I saw my own fucking guts hanging out, mucker.'

A medical orderly came up, as weary, filthy, and unshaven as the rest of us, moving down the column of mules. He pushed me out of the way to examine Geordie's securing straps.

'Is he – ?' I asked.

'We're moving this batch of wounded off straightaway. This bloke's had a jab of morphine, so he's not suffering pain. Is he a mucker of yours?'

I bit my bottom lip. 'One of the best,' I said, and for some reason the words started me crying.

In my ammo pouch, against the sten magazines, I had stuffed the picture of Hanuman. I pulled it out, creased, stained, and folded, and tucked it into Geordie's shirt, against his clammy chest.

'It's the old Monkey God, Geordie, remember? The Monkey God ... Look after him for me!'

'The Monkey God ...'

Geordie was the only bastard in the squad who hadn't kidded me about Hanuman, Vishnu, and the rest. As I stared down at his pallid ugly face, my tears came again,

[261]

and I turned my head away so that the Pathans would not notice.

When I looked again, the line of mules was already moving away through the nearest trees. Geordie would be lucky if he made it back to base-hospital. Hanuman wasn't going to be much help.

With victory – with the minor victory of Aradura, our mood changed. We had survived, and Aradura was one jungle-mountain we would never have to climb again! For a while there was not even the need to keep our heads down.

As the patrols were bringing in their shit-stained prisoners, the RAF finished making an air-drop of ammo, water, fags, and rations on Aradura. 'A' Company was getting its share under the watchful eyes of RSM Payne and Inskipp. Inskipp had a shoulder wound and his left arm was out of action, but he refused to be evacuated.

I sat in one of the bunkers, talking to Wally as he operated our wireless set under Boyer's supervision. Casualty reports coming in suggested that the Mendips had suffered less badly than we feared.

'We didn't live in vain, Wally,' I said.

He clapped me on the back, right across my prickly heat. 'That's God's truth, me smelly old mate! I bet you was praying to your fucking old monkey god this time yesterday, weren't you?!'

'Who were you praying to, Churchill?'

'Come orf it, Stubby, I been keeping myself morally pure lately – that's what did it!'

'You haven't got much fucking choice in this neck of the woods, have you? You know old Geordie got a packet didn't you?'

'Yeah. Poor old Geordie! I reckon he's had his fucking

chips. Right in the fucking guts. . .' Wally screwed his face up as if thinking. 'Nice old lad, Geordie – his trouble was, he didn't believe in anything.'

Without arguing with Wally – always a useless occupation – I was unconvinced by this implied reason for Geordie's packet. After all, I had survived so far, and what did I believe in?

'Oh, fuck!' I said. 'What a fucking fornicating shower it all is!'

Aylmer came over, bringing us two packets of cigarettes and a half-*piyala* of rum-and-water each. While Wally got on with Boyer's messages, Aylmer and I sat on one side, smoking and sipping our drink.

'This rum should help my dysentery!'

'Yes, it'll clear it up like one o'clock! In the old days, surgeons used to give their patients rum before they sawed their legs off. Without it, nobody would have survived the ordeal.'

We watched the Japs being marshalled into bundles by Harding and Charley Cox. When Harding and Charley got their cigarette issue, they lit up and then, rather sheepishly, offered one to the nearest Japs.

'That's the way to kill the little bleeders off!', Wally remarked, looking round from the set. 'Give 'em a de Reske!'

Bamber, who was near Charley, called out angrily, 'Hey, Charley, don't give those bastards a drag! They'd kill you if they had the chance – they were shooting our fucking mates yesterday!'

'Don't worry, I'll shoot 'em if they try anything, but they're human same as we are,' Charley said cheerfully.

'Not in my fucking book, they aren't,' Bamber said, and he turned away.

We had secured Peter, a lonely pimple on a big ridge. But the sitreps coming over the air were startlingly bad. Nobody else had any joy on ill-fated Aradura. The Royal Welch had been forced back, owing to impossible fighting country as much as anything, and the rest of the battalion had had to move back for lack of support. We were alone on Aradura, and the situation looked grave. We were ordered to dig in.

'A' and 'B' Companies were now all within one perimeter, and familiar faces were missing. My old pal Chota Morris had been killed by grenades while leading No. 1 Platoon forward. Handsome Hansom and Ginger Gascadden were dead. It turned into a bad day, despite the charge that had come from our success; everyone was very quiet.

Only late in the afternoon was there cause for cheer. The high ground of Peter allowed us a view of the road. It wound below us, down the glittering hillside. Our artillery was pounding Garage Spur, on the other side of the valley. We could see paddy fields, with Nagas working in them as if nothing was happening. And one of our mobile columns was moving down the road from Kohima! It could not be too long before reinforcements moved up the *khud* to join us, if only we could hang on where we were.

Reaction set in then. The lull in the fighting gave time for thought. That was the afternoon I really got the jitters. By next morning, stuck on that fucking hill in the middle of miles of wilderness, we might all be dead. And I thought of old Geordie, suffering total aggs.

Nothing ever happened out in Assam as you expected it to. We had plenty of defensive patrols out during the night. They came back with nothing to report. There was no firing. No Japs were contacted. The rain fell. It was still falling at first light, when Sergeant Gowland came in with a patrol and reported that the Japs seemed to have disappeared from the ridge. That was the last day of May.

It was two days before we could confirm that Aradura was

clear, and confirmatory reports came in from elsewhere. For the first time, the Japs were in retreat. Sato had had enough; he had given the order to withdraw! His battered forces were in retreat south, towards Imphal and the distant Chindwin!

We came down the mountain again, taking our prisoners with us.

The road below us was open and the polyglot Fourteenth Army rolling through. At last we said good-bye to Aradura and stood on the road! Inskipp marched us to a point where a mess and a bath unit had been set up in a broken and deserted hamlet. The mess was a *basha* without a roof; the benches and tables looked like the height of civilization. There stood our fat cooks in their greasy green vests, cocky as ever, Ron Rusk and George Locke.

'How're you doing, Stubby, boy? How's your belly off for spots?' Rusk had abandoned his old cry, 'Get in, pigs, it's all swill!'

'Still burning the *bergoo*, Ruskie? I didn't think they'd let you *admis* this near the firing line!'

'You want to watch what you're saying to him,' Locke said, digging his mate in his ribs and nodding at me. 'Ron killed a Jap single-handed yesterday – coshed him over the bonce with a ladle, didn't you, Rusky Boy?'

'The little bastard walked into the cookhouse and I coshed him one!'

This heroic deed of Rusk's became legendary. It was useless to point out that the Jap in question had probably been on his last legs anyway; Rusk had made a kill, and thereafter it was hopeless complaining about the food or we would be warned that we should get what the Jap got – a cosh over the bonce with a ladle.

At that meal there were no complaints. We sat at the

benches and ate real meat, which someone suggested was our old friend the elephant from Merema Ridge. There was beer with the meat and vegetables, Yankee Beer from Milwaukee, with peaches and condensed milk to follow, and a *piyala* full of *char*.

It was a very quiet meal. No one spoke, no one looked at anyone else, until Charley Cox said, producing the fruit of long consideration, 'They're fucking brave bastards, the Japs, all the same.'

'Bravest bastards in the world, after the Fourteenth Army,' Wally agreed.

Silence again, until Charley went on. 'You know all the balls-ups our Higher-Ups made? I mean, like about withdrawing amphibious support and everything? It was lucky the Jap Higher-Ups made balls-ups too, wasn't it? What I mean to say, if they'd gone straight for Dimapur before we got to Zubza, instead of waiting to mop up Kohima . . . well, there wouldn't have been anything to stop 'em, would there?'

'They'd be in Calcutta, eating in Firpo's by now,' Dusty Miller said.

'That's what I mean – their Higher-Ups made a balls-up same as ours.'

'The biggest balls-up was starting the war in the first place,' old Bamber said. 'Where's it get you?'

'To fucking Milestone 61,' Wally said.

Silence fell again as we tackled the peaches.

Afterwards, we gathered in the clearing. Inskipp stood up on his jeep and addressed us, thanking us for incredible bravery under adverse conditions. He read out an order of the day from General Grover, Divisional Commander, congratulating all ranks and stating that the enemy was in full retreat. It was our duty now to get after him and not let a man escape. Then Inskipp went off to have his arm attended to.

After the meal and speech, baths. The baths were built out of big oil-drums, cut in half lengthways, and were full of wonderful hot water. Easing off our foetid boots, shedding our shitty uniforms, we climbed in.

What luxury! Our aches and pains were forgotten as we soaked. Things might be bad again, but they could never be as bad as they had been.

Slumped back in the water, we began to sing sentimental things, *There's A Long Long Trail A-Winding, I Can't Give You Anything But Love, Side by Side, Underneath The Arches.*

We could see lorries rolling by along the road, loaded with troops heading towards Imphal, still beleaguered.

'Get some fucking service in!' we bellowed. Full of fun, the Mendips were, given half a chance!

While we were still wallowing – the orderlies could not get us out – a Dodge truck bumped up and stopped beside us.

'Any of you ginks want your backs scrubbed?' It was McGuffie, turning up with the quarter-master-sergeant and a stack of new jungle-green uniforms.

I bellowed to him, 'Jock, you skiving old base-*wallah*, come over here!'

'You can wash your own mankey fucking back, Stubbs – I know where it's been!'

Cries from all sides – 'Where've you been hiding, you sly old sod?'

Jock shook his head. 'While you lazy fuckers have been up in the hills screwing Naga women, I've been working my fucking arse off at Kohima.'

'You never worked in your life, Jock.'

'Och away with ye, man, I've been weaving a new net for the D.C.'s tennis court! And I've brought you all new uniforms.'

'Get dried and I'll kit you out, lads,' the QMS said. 'Form a line as you're ready.'

It was while we were trying out blouses and trousers and boots that he told us the news. The Second Front had opened in Europe that morning. A bridgehead had been established on the Normandy beaches and the British and Americans were pouring in.

'They must be using our fucking landing-craft!' Wally said, and we all fell about laughing. It was 6 June, 1944. We had forgotten date and season.

It took a time to remember Kohima, so long had we spent on Aradura. When Jock was asked, he said, 'It's all clear of Japs now. They pulled out there, same as here – couldn't stand the smell of the Mendips. The battle lasted seventy days. They're holding film shows at Assam Barracks now – I saw Margaret Lockwood last night, wobbling her titties at James Mason. You boys want to get around a bit!'

'Margaret Lockwood! Ooorgh!' There was a general statement of what we could and couldn't do to Margaret Lockwood. The arts of peace were already struggling to reassert themselves.

'What's that round your *pughri*, Jock?' I asked.

Jock removed his smart bush hat and polished it with the ginger hairs of his left arm, while gazing admiringly at the bright orange fabric tied round the crown. 'Margaret Lockwood would go for me in this outfit, don't ye think? It's a bit of one of the parachutes as dumps the rations. I was in charge of collecting them yesterday – bloody nigh got killed with them damn great crates falling *nichi!* You young lads don't know what danger is until you've been up the airstrip.'

Bamber came along frowning and towelling his hairy crutch. 'You want to *chibber ao* and shut your gob, McFuckingGuffie, you do! You don't know what the word danger means until you been up against the Japs on Aradura. I lost some of me best mates up there, so you shit in it!'

'I know how you feel, Bamber,' Jock said, sympathetically. 'You'll be away to see Margaret Lockwood tonight and then you'll feel better.'

'No, I won't. I don't want to see Margaret Fucking Lockwood.'

'Suit yourself, mate.'

I looked at them both, thinking I understood how both felt.

Even this fearful time of battle was precious to me, just because it wasn't going to last. The jungles, like the cities, came and went.

Suddenly it struck me – I had an infinite capacity for happiness! I was really a hell of a feller!

My elevated mood endured for the rest of the day. Wearing our new kit, we marched a mile down the road – the Manipur Road! – to a temporary camp, where we boiled rifles and stens through with hot water and fresh four-b'-two in our pull-throughs.

There was no chance of getting up to the flicks in Kohima that night – in the morning, we would be moving forward again. But McGuffie drove down in his truck and brought some rum along. We sat on the tailboard chatting, and he told a long tedious story about how he had nearly come to blows with an Irish cook in the DLI.

I heard Aylmer limping along, still singing his pathetic fragment of song, 'Could I but see thee stand before me . . .'

'D'ye want a *piyala* of rum, mate?' Jock asked him.

'Where did you get it from?' Aylmer asked. 'Did you lift it?'

'My guts has no' been too gude – fucking *krab*, in fact. I needed something for them, and this stuff settles them fine. Stubby's got the same complaint and he's feeling better already, aren't you, Stubby?'

'Did you lift it?'

'Bollucks to that for a question! This fucking rum was meant to come up to you bastards up on Aradura, if you must know, but we couldne get it there, so I took charge of it. You wouldn't want the mules to drink it, would you? I'm offering it to you now.'

'You can keep it, Jock,' Aylmer said mildly, and marched off.

[269]

Jock laughed. 'You lot are fucking shell-shocked or *puggle* or something!'

'We're just proud, Jock, that's all.'

'Proud you didn't bloody get killed?! Och, I wasne killed myself, was I?

'Away and piss up your kilt, Jock! We won the fucking battle, didn't we?'

'This fucking Burma campaign has only just started, do you *malum* that? We'll probably all be dead in another six months. How many years do you think it's going to take to chase the Japs out of all these great mankey hills?'

He swung his hand up and pointed into the darkness, where the hillsides stood.

I could not say anything to him. Suddenly I was shagged out. He had not been with us and could not understand.

More gently, he said, 'How many fucking years is it going to take to chase the fucking Japs out of this bloody place? I'm asking you, man, only asking. You're the fucking soldier!'

No good arguing that. 'Jock, I know I've asked you before, but what were you in Civvy Street?'

'Och, man, I was a waiter in the Gleneagles Hotel. I thought I'd told you.'

It struck me as funny at the time. 'I'm sorry to laugh, Jock – I'm shagged to the wide. I must go and get my head down.'

'You learn a lot, being a waiter, ye ken. I was serving at table while you was going to school with cake in your hand.'

'Sure, Jock, I know. I wasn't really laughing, honest! You know my mate Geordie got badly shot up, up on Aradura?'

He patted my shoulder, and he was not a man who ever touched people. 'Don't greet over it! He was a poor wee turd of a man, and you know it – asking to get fucking shot!'

'He's probably bloody dead by now.'

'So's a whole lot of other fuckers, including a lot of brave

Jocks, but you've got to soldier on, haven't you? I learnt *that* fucking lesson waiting at table. At least they nailed old Spunk Bucket, so there's some justice in the world! Now for Christ's sake come and sup some stolen rum and talk of something cheery!'

When I could, I left him. There would be time for Jock later – perhaps a lot later. I was going to get my head down early and give myself a bloody good going over to celebrate survival. My sense of personal freedom was still with me. I had survived. It could never be expressed in words, all of which belonged to systems; but it was going to be expressed in an outburst of hand-fucking, with the pukka thing to follow just as soon as possible.

You've got to soldier on . . .

A troop of armoured cars, followed by infantry in carriers, rolled along the road, heading towards Phesama. Fighting was going on there; as Jock said, there was still trouble to come.

I noticed there were several Mendips standing solitary, like myself, watching by the side of the road; the sight of them became terribly moving. They were smoking, watching the transport, thinking. We had all been together; now we had come apart again. Suddenly, it occured to me that perhaps they too saw themselves as just pretending to be Mendips!

But that was all balls, really. Tomorrow, we would be moving into action again at Viswema, where forward elements of 8 Brigade were already engaged – when, again, there would be no room for anything but action and the pressure for survival.

A heavy drop of rain landed on my cheek. The clouds rose over the valley, mounting high above the dark shoulders of Pulebadze. As I headed towards my *charpoy*, I reformed the image of the Naga girl whose body had momentarily been close to mine on Merema Ridge. She had orchids in her sleek hair. She raised her skirt suggestively. She smiled and gave me the old come-hither.

Before I reached my blankets, I was gratified to feel a stirring in my trousers. Probably every man-jack in the Mendips had his hand on his knob that night, giving thanks for survival.

The early monsoon rain began to fall over our positions. Down the road, the guns were pounding away at Viswema.